THE INDUSTRIAL ARCHAEOLOGY
OF HERTFORDSHIRE

THE INDUSTRIAL ARCHAEOLOGY
OF THE BRITISH ISLES

Series Editor: E. R. R. GREEN

Derbyshire, by Frank Nixon
The East Midlands, by David M. Smith
Hertfordshire, by W. Branch Johnson
The Lake Counties, by J. D. Marshall and M. Davies-Shiel
Lancashire, by Owen Ashmore
Scotland, by John Butt
Southern England (second edition, revised), by Kenneth Hudson

ASSOCIATED VOLUMES

The Bristol Region, by R. A. Buchanan and Neil Cossons
Dartmoor, by Helen Harris
Gloucestershire Woollen Mills, by Jennifer Tann
Stone Blocks and Iron Rails, by Bertram Baxter
The Tamar Valley, by Frank Booker
Techniques of Industrial Archaeology, by J. P. M. Pannell

OTHER INDUSTRIAL HISTORY

The British Iron and Steel Industry, by W. K. V. Gale
The Early Factory Masters, by Stanley D. Chapman
The Engineering Industry of the North of Ireland, by W. E. Coe
The History of Water Power in Ulster, by H. D. Gribbon

All these books are in uniform format

.

The Industrial Archaeology of
HERTFORDSHIRE

W. BRANCH JOHNSON
FSA FRHistS

DAVID & CHARLES: NEWTON ABBOT

7153 4775 6

In gratitude
to
D. J. Capper and 88 SNK,
without both of whom my knowledge
of the county's industrial archaeology
would be a great deal less

*Set in Imprint, 11 pt 2 pt leaded
and printed in Great Britain by
Latimer Trend & Company Limited Plymouth
for David & Charles (Publishers) Limited
South Devon House   Newton Abbot   Devon*

Contents

List of Illustrations

PLATES

Plates not otherwise acknowledged are from the author's own collection

IN TEXT

The county boundary shown in the maps is the pre-1965 one, which includes Barnet and East Barnet. In that year Hertfordshire lost both to Greater London, but gained Potters Bar.

PART ONE

CHAPTER ONE

The Hertfordshire Background

HERTFORDSHIRE is the birthplace of Sir Henry Bessemer, the ancestral home of the Canal Duke, the last home of John Loudon McAdam, the cradle of the malting industry in Britain and the scene of the development of modern papermaking techniques. Nevertheless the chief problem it presents to industrial archaeologists is that of equating it with counties whose richness in industrial monuments important to the history of technology keep them in the forefront of the study. At first glance they may be disposed to write the county off altogether. Yet marginal though it may be from their point of view, it has its own legitimate place, in that, while most of its present-day industries are twentieth-century importations and thus of rather less significance, others—those with which this book is for the most part concerned—are rooted in the history, some in the very nature of the county.

With its southern rim never more than twenty miles distant from the heart of London, with neither coal nor mineral deposits and with an area of only 630 square miles, Hertfordshire has always been predominantly agricultural—indeed agriculture remained the principal occupation of its inhabitants down to the Second World War, and even today some 65 per cent of its land is in agricultural use. While during the eighteenth and nineteenth centuries considerable areas of the countryside elsewhere were being transformed by the process of the Industrial Revolution, this long agricultural tradition was sedulously fostered by Hertfordshire squires, most of whom were professional or commercial magnates in London, who regarded their country estates as refuges from metropolitan bustle and discouraged rather than encouraged anything likely to disturb rural peace—which may in part account for the high prices, observable in eighteenth-century newspapers, paid for Hertfordshire country houses. Nor did the turnpiking of roads bring about any appreciable industrial development: then as now, Hertfordshire was regarded as a 'transit' county to be got through as quickly as possible on the way to somewhere else, only its inns being worth attention. Canal and river navigations tended to boost one or two already long-established industries rather than to introduce new ones; and early railways, generally speaking, led quite as much to residential and commuter as to industrial development. Wherever we look, Hertfordshire industries remained rooted in the county's agricultural past until they were swamped by a mass of importations in the present century.

Until the Middle Ages the county was forested almost everywhere, though more densely in the western, Chiltern, area and in the south than in the east. During the gradual clearing of the woodland in medieval times, widespread charcoal burning naturally occurred, apparently to produce charcoal for export as well as for local use; in 1475 for example, Sir John Say's manors round Little Berkhampstead are stated to have sent 62 loads of charcoal to London. Writing in 1564, William Bullein describes a man and his wife fleeing before an outbreak of plague in London; at Barnet the wife asks, 'What great smoke is in yonder wood? God grant it be well.' To which the husband replies, 'It is nothing but making of charcoal in that place.'[1] At Stanstead Abbots in 1606 Richard Keelinge was in trouble with the Justices over his charcoal firing, both inhabitants and strangers being, it was stated, 'constrained to stop their noses, the stink is so great'. One of the last references to charcoal burning is in Arthur Young's *General View of the Agriculture of Hertfordshire* (1804), when he speaks of the burning of beeches for charcoal in the Earl of Clarendon's park at the Grove, Watford; but it is still remembered in such place names as Cole Green, Coles Grove, Coles Hill, Colemans Green and Colliers End.

---

[1] Only in 1965 did Barnet and East Barnet leave Hertfordshire to become part of the Greater London borough of Barnet; Hertfordshire acquired Potters Bar. For postal purposes Barnet is still in Hertfordshire.

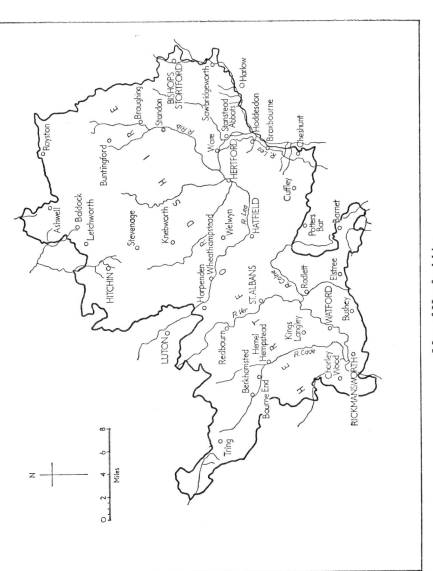

Map of Hertfordshire

The other ancient industry based naturally on the county's wood-land resources was wood turning, with Berkhamsted and Cheshunt as its principal centres. In the eighteenth century, William Ellis, agricultural writer (and delightful gossip) of Little Gaddesden, declares that those two towns alone 'make more consumption of this wood [alder] and beech than any other two towns in Great Britain, as is allowed by good judges'. Chair frames, barrel staves, bowls, tent pegs, shovels, brooms, spoons, hurdles, all continued to be made at Berkhamsted throughout the nineteenth century; and at Berk-hamsted and Ware barges were built down to about 1910, for use on the Grand Junction (now Union) Canal and river Lea respectively. Though the barge-building industry is now dead, East & Sons Ltd, joinery manufacturers, still thrive in Berkhamsted, where Job East settled in 1840 after moving from Buckinghamshire, and where a bandsaw by Greenwood of Batley, Yorks, dated 1861, is still operated, alongside other nineteenth-century equipment.

By far the most important agricultural products of Hertfordshire were (and still are) barley and wheat; in the early eighteenth century it was written that, 'Hertfordshire barley is so much prized in London that many hundred quarters are sold by that name in a year, of which not a grain was ever sown in this county.' This abundant barley yield gave rise to the county's oldest and richest industry—malting—which was carried on in all districts but had its biggest centres at Ware, Hertford and, later, Bishop's Stortford. The industry is described more fully in the next chapter; here it is enough to say that it was in existence at Ware in the early Middle Ages, possibly earlier, the barley coming by packhorse or wagon not only from with-in the county but also from adjoining counties to the north and north-east; malt was sent out by packhorse or by boat on the Lea to London. Bishop's Stortford trade expanded after the opening of the Stort Navigation in 1766 and from then until near the end of the nineteenth century the industry flourished in all three towns. In recent years, and owing to a variety of causes, is has seriously de-clined but is still carried on at Ware, Stanstead Abbots, Sawbridge-

Page 17   (above) *Nineteenth-century malting at Stanstead Abbots;*
(below) *from malting to dwelling house at Bishop's Stortford*

Page 18 (above) *King's Langley Church Hall formerly a malting built in 1826;* (below) *interior of Lion malting, Baldock, showing tamped chalk floor*

worth, Baldock and Bishop's Stortford, while old malting sites, now derelict or adapted to other uses, are found all over the county.

Allied to malting is brewing. As in every other county, early brewers in Hertfordshire served only local markets; or, from the second half of the eighteenth century, their own tied houses within a restricted area. There was certainly a brewery of some size at Watford in the early years of the seventeenth century and others in such towns as St Albans and Hertford; by the middle of the nineteenth century Hertfordshire had, in all, several dozen brewing firms, which by bankruptcy, closure for other reasons or amalgamation are now reduced to three—the genuinely Hertfordshire firm of McMullen Ltd at Hertford; Greene King Ltd of Bury St Edmunds, Suffolk, operating a small brewery at Furneux Pelham; and Ind Coope Ltd, of whom Benskin Ltd of Watford are a component. Amongst them these three companies own a large proportion of Hertfordshire's public houses—some 880; most of the remainder are owned by Flowers Breweries Ltd, now amalgamated with Whitbread Ltd, who do not brew in the county.

A by-product of Hertfordshire wheat growing was the industry of straw plaiting and straw hat making which flourished from the seventeenth century down to the First World War. Straw plaiting was entirely a cottage industry carried on by women and children; the supplement to low agricultural wages that it contributed to innumerable households may, it has been suggested, account in part at least for Hertfordshire's tardy adherence to early trade unionism. Straw hat making had a centre of some size in St Albans but a bigger one just outside the county at Luton in Bedfordshire. These industries are dealt with in greater detail in Chapter Three.

Hertfordshire lies on chalk which is partially overlain in the east and south by London clay. These geological conditions provided the resources for the development of lime burning in the west and tile and brickmaking elsewhere, industries that are now extinct. The Romans made tiles at Radlett, where a tile and brick field operated as late as the 1920s. Tiles were being made at Codicote and other villages

B

soon after the Black Death and in 1430 a kiln near Little Berkhampstead made 'tiles called bricks'. Bricks continued to be made at Welwyn until about 1930, at Ware until even more recently, and there is still a small brickfield at Stonyhills, north of Hertford. At Colliers End, north of Ware, is an underground kiln associated with a brickfield that was worked until about 1920; this kiln, which is circular, about 25 ft in diameter, with a central firebox, is interesting because it is roofed with sixteenth-century brick, though its use can be traced back only to the late eighteenth century. Presumably the bricks are the spoil of a now vanished Tudor house.

A curiosity of Hertfordshire brickmaking is the patenting by Caleb Hitch of Ware in 1828 of bricks, roughly 12 in by 6 in by 6 in, each brick having flanges and cavities designed, by an elaborate system of interlocking, to economise in mortar and increase structural strength. They are to be seen in a number of house and boundary walls in Ware, in a bridge at Watton and in surrounding villages as far away as Wakeley Farm, near Westmill; but one imagines that their weight, to say nothing of the jigsaw-like complexities of their moulding, would be far from acceptable to the average bricklayer. For how long they continued to use it is hard to determine; the present building firm of Frederick Hitch Ltd of Ware knows nothing of them.

Hertfordshire builders in the past adopted the frequent practice, very helpful to all who investigate ancient buildings, of inserting into a wall a brick inscribed with the date of erection and sometimes with the initials of the owner—that is, apart from more formal and elaborate dating designs on, for instance, manor houses. Such bricks are found (though they are often far from easy to detect) in all parts of the county and in buildings of all kinds, ranging from the early seventeenth to the late nineteenth centuries. On the chimney of a Hertford brewery, demolished in 1967, could be seen near the top the date of its erection, 1885, and in a long descending procession the initials of the owner, his wife, all his children and certain remote members of his family.

It would appear that during the eighteenth century a few small industries were located temporarily in the county, though only an enormous amount of detailed research could hope to discover all. Of the three following examples culled at random, two were in small villages away from turnpike roads or any obvious means of communication for the marketing of their products. The first is the establishment in about 1761 of a calico printing works at Woolmers, Hertingfordbury, by John Collins, whose Dublin works had closed down a couple of years earlier. All that is known of this enterprise is that Land Tax returns from that year to 1772 give Woolmers to Godfrey and Collins (nothing is known of Godfrey) and that local Militia Lists over the same period include a number of calico printers and one engineer. Certain of Collins's designs are inscribed 'Collins Woolmers' and dated. It may be added that Woolmers was rebuilt some twenty years later by the Duke of Bridgewater.

The second temporary industry has only one reference—in the diary of a Bramfield farmer, John Carrington, when he records the death of Robert Gass in 1804:

> He was brought from London by one Thomas Rightbright, an optician, about the year 1760, who took Tewin Mill, which was a corn mill, and at great expense altered it into a glass mill for polishing convex and concave glasses and spectacles etc. and no admittance for anyone to see the same for years. But Rightbright and his wife dying, one Flindall, his foreman, took it, but old Mr Schreiber, the landlord, dying, the son wanted more rent. Therefore Flindall left it, and in the year 1803 it was taken by one Cannon of Welwyn and made a corn mill again after upwards of forty years a glass mill.

Thirdly, there was a mill at St Albans used for polishing diamonds, which also operated during the second half of the century. Nothing, however, is known of it, except that by the early nineteenth century it had turned from polishing diamonds to the spinning of cotton wicks for candles, for which it seems to have been used for about thirty years.

But a few more permanent industries as well were either established or expanded towards the close of the eighteenth century—notably rural-based papermaking, silk throwing at Watford (both of which receive fuller consideration later) and urban-based printing.

There may have been a printer at St Albans in the late fifteenth century, who produced the famous *Book of St Albans*, but his existence has been disputed. There was a second, better authenticated, in the sixteenth century. Then for two centuries no other is heard of in Hertfordshire, probably because of parliamentary restriction of the trade to London, the universities and a handful of great cities. But in 1768 there came to Hertford the man who was to found by far the oldest printing firm still existing in the county. He was Stephen Austin.

Of Yorkshire birth, Austin in his youth had worked for John Kearsley of London, the bookseller closely associated with Wilkes's *North Briton*; when Kearsley went bankrupt in 1764 young Austin, though still in a junior capacity, appears to have carried on the firm for some time. Establishing himself as a stationer at Hertford four years later, he soon undertook printing as well and in 1772 (probably under the influence of Wilkes) started there a Radical newspaper, the *Hartford Mercury*, of which no original copy survives. When the East India Company founded a college for its budding servants, at first (1804) in Hertford Castle, later (1809) at Haileybury on Hertford Heath, both Austin's son, another Stephen, and his Hertford competitor, George Simpson (whose firm still continues as Simpson Shand Ltd) officially sold stationery and textbooks (and, less officially, cribs) to the students; and it was the younger Stephen who first undertook the printing and publishing for the college of oriental texts, a service for which the house has since become famous. Meanwhile, and true to the family's Radical tradition, the younger Stephen and his son, a third Stephen, published the *Hertford Reformer* in 1834, which, after various changes of title and the absorption of the *County Press*, originally founded by Simpson, still continues as the now non-political *Herts Mercury*. Since 1909 Stephen Austin & Sons Ltd have been associated with Harrison & Sons Ltd of London.

It may be added as a matter of interest that, on the closure of the East India College at Haileybury in 1857, the third Stephen Austin was a prime mover in its re-opening as a public school nine years later.

In the days of the first Stephen Austin other printers are heard of here and there—T. Baldwin at Cheshunt in 1778, William McDowell at Berkhamsted in 1793, J. Bedford at Hitchin in 1800. Under an Act of 1798 designed to prevent seditious publication, licences to others were issued in succeeding years; among the most interesting is that to Richard Gibbs of St Albans in 1826. It was Richard's son who produced the first *St Albans Times* in 1855 (the year of the abolition of the Newspaper Stamp Duty), which eleven years later became the *Herts Advertiser*, still in the hands of Gibbs & Bamforth Ltd.

After the turnpiking of the highways radiating north and north-west from London, in the eighteenth century, such industrial development as occurred along their routes was insignificant; indeed the chief effect was to enhance the importance of a few towns and villages as local craft centres. These roads carried enormous quantities of county agricultural produce to London markets, bringing back abundant and very varied refuse to manure Hertfordshire's hungry soil; they served too as improved routes for cattle-droving from Wales and the Midlands to Barnet Fair and London slaughterers; and they provided, of course, some of the most famous coaching routes. A few of the inns to which they brought prosperity are listed in the Gazetteer.

The opening of the Grand Junction Canal in 1800 seems at first to have had very little effect upon Hertfordshire; nor at first did the coming of the London and Birmingham Railway through Watford in 1837 and Tring in 1838. 'The London and Birmingham Railway', said Robson's *Directory of Herts* in 1838, 'is, however, calculated to suspend all intercourse by stage coach. . . . It remains to be seen what effect will be produced on the local circumstances of the county of Hertford by so important and sudden a change.' It is perhaps symbolic that, when Queen Victoria passed through Hitchin soon after the opening of the Great Northern Railway in 1850, the station was decorated with straw plait, while Biggleswade station in Bedfordshire was festooned with carrots.

Nearer London a steady residential expansion followed the opening of the Great Northern, particularly around Barnet; to East Barnet, with 663 inhabitants in 1851, was soon added an entirely railway-created New Barnet, not mentioned in the 1851 Census but with nearly 8,000 people in 1871 and today with 40,000. Similar but less spectacular population increases had followed the Northern and Eastern Railway development (later the Great Eastern) in the Lea valley towns of Hoddesdon and Cheshunt after 1842. The Midland Railway did not pass through St Albans until 1868 but led there to the same result—as did the coming of the Metropolitan Railway to Rickmansworth in 1887. It is of course obvious that railway communication was always a factor in encouraging the establishment of new businesses in the county; but industrial development seems to have come to Hertfordshire only gradually and under other pressures, to judge by the evidence about the end of the century. About that time, one may note the rise of certain local craftsmen, especially blacksmiths, to the status of agricultural engineers. Typical are F. Bracey & Sons of Benington; at Ware, D. Wickham & Co Ltd from being purely local ironworkers entered the general engineering business in 1896.

A glance through Kelly's *Directory of Herts*, 1902, confirms the long agricultural tradition of the county, in spite of the number of small industrial firms to be found in it; but in the following year an event took place which was a herald of change. That event was the founding in 1903 of the first Garden City at Letchworth.

Ebenezer (later Sir Ebenezer) Howard's courage in actually beginning to build a self-contained town accommodating industry and residents in separately planned areas and surrounded by a belt of open country was at that time revolutionary, less crack-brained to idealists and cranks than to businessmen bound by tradition to overcrowded London and well aware that Letchworth was 34 miles off, on neither a main line of railway nor a direct London road. For some years the difficulty of persuading them out of their timidity helped to keep the affairs of the First Garden City Company in low water; the earliest notable industrial accession to the struggling experiment was that of the publishing firm of J. M. Dent & Sons Ltd, who have printed their Everyman Library and numerous other works on the firm's lists at Letchworth since 1906. In 1910 came the Spirella Co Ltd, corset makers, in 1912 Marmet Baby Carriages Ltd and in 1920 British Tabulating Machines Co Ltd, now International Computers & Tabulaters Ltd. Today a great variety of light engineering is carried on there, vehicle building, rubber manufacture, parachute making, and food processing. Letchworth's sister garden city, near Welwyn, founded by Howard in 1920, has ICI (Plastics Division), Roche Pharmaceutical Products Ltd, Nabisco Foods, and a total range quite as great as that of Letchworth.

It was perhaps the wide, even though sometimes derisory, publicity that Letchworth received in its early days that helped to draw attention to Hertfordshire's potential attractions for businessmen. But not wholly: Watford had (as we shall see later) already become its most important industrial centre; near that town, the Gade valley attracted such large enterprises as Ovaltine Ltd and saw the rapid development of the paper mills of John Dickinson & Co Ltd between Apsley, Hemel Hempstead and Croxley, Rickmansworth. St Albans, Hertford and the Lea valley towns all received their quota of new factories, though towns in the north of the county (Letchworth apart) remained less affected. Even before the First World War motion picture making had been established at Boreham Wood by Ideal Pictures Ltd; Boreham Wood and Elstree, for long oases of rural quiet, are now the home of far more varied industries, though motion pictures are still made there. After 1918 industry of many kinds exploded into the county on a scale hitherto unknown, chiefly if not entirely from London. Though to single out one rather than another is perhaps invidious, mention of the aircraft industry can scarcely be avoided. In 1930 the De Havilland Aircraft Co Ltd, now Hawker

Siddeley Aviation Ltd, transformed Hatfield from being primarily the historic home of the Cecil family, Marquesses of Salisbury, into something much more lively—and noisy.[1] About a dozen years later Handley Page Ltd followed,[2] moving from Hendon, Middlesex, to Colney Street near St Albans. After the Second World War came three government-sponsored, self-contained New Towns—at Stevenage, Hemel Hempstead and, jointly, Welwyn Garden City and Hatfield—with a fourth just over the county boundary at Harlow, Essex; each quickly acquired a thriving industrial area, comprising firms that are household names but also many small ones. In the last twenty-five years the outward movement from London has increased enormously and shows little sign of slackening—nor, of course, does the residential expansion that inevitably accompanies it. Today much of the southern part of the county is given over to industry and housing, usually more or less concentrated into well-defined areas but sometimes scattered, and also to extensive gravel digging. Elsewhere towns are steadily developing small industrial accretions and house prices in even remote villages soar fantastically—it is fortunate for Hertfordshire that its County Planning Department is an active and alert one.

In the industrial hierarchy of the county, in terms of the number of men employed first come aircraft and aircraft components manufacturing, second light engineering and third papermaking. These are followed by the many distributive trades that are needed to satisfy a population that has trebled in three-quarters of a century—a greater population increase than that of any other county.

Yet, despite these enormous developments, only in 1951 did agriculture cease to head the list of employment sectors, being for the first time exceeded by industry in general. Even today the centre of the county is quite as much occupied by agriculture as by all other

---

[1] It was not at Hatfield but at Salisbury Hall, Shenley, that De Havilland designed and built the first Mosquito aircraft early in 1940. It was dismantled, taken to Hatfield and flown from there. The second was taken to Hatfield intact.

[2] Taken over in 1969 by the Cravens Corporation of St. Louis, USA.

land uses; astonishingly rural pockets remain in the south between Potters Bar and Cheshunt and between Welwyn Garden City, Hitchin and Luton, in Bedfordshire. In the whole north-eastern triangle between Bishop's Stortford, Buntingford and Royston, the explorer may well find it difficult to believe that he is, in fact, within forty miles of the Tower of London—that is, of course, if, as was still possible when this book went to press, London's third airport is not established right in the middle of it, at Nuthampstead.

CHAPTER TWO

Malting and Brewing, Milling and Papermaking

THESE four occupations, all dependent in varying degrees upon the agricultural nature of the county, represent Hertfordshire's longest-standing contributions to the industrial scene. All four are still carried on, though, with the exception of papermaking, less extensively than in the past.

MALTING

In *The Brewing Industry in England 1700–1830* Peter Mathias speaks of the region centred on Ware, Hoddesdon and Stanstead Abbots as 'the oldest and most mature malting area in the country'. 'The gentle valley of the Lea and the Stort', he adds, 'may be seen as the cradle of the industry in Britain.' From the Middle Ages malting is heard of in many parts of Hertfordshire, not only in the Lea and Stort valleys but also at Hitchin, Baldock, St Albans, Ashwell, Aldenham and other places. It was Ware, however, that by its strategic position had already inevitably become the industry's focal point. The great Roman highway, called (though not by the Romans) Ermine Street and now A10, passed through the town from Hertfordshire's richest barley-growing areas, from the barley fields of Huntingdon and within easy reach of barley-growing Northamptonshire on the north-west and Cambridgeshire and East Anglia on the north-east. The road continued southwards to London, always an insatiable market for malt. Through Ware too flowed the Lea, more or less navigable in spite of neglect; and just below Ware it was joined by the Stort, flowing through Bishop's Stortford.

In 1646 complaint was made to the county justices of 'the great loads of malt from both the Hadhams, Albury, Stortford, all the Pelhams and Clavering [Essex] through Ware Extra [Wareside] and the excessive loads from Norwich, Bury [St Edmunds] and Cambridge weekly, the teams often consisting of seven or eight horses. There is a great increase of maltsters in Ware.' Rather less than twenty years afterwards, in 1663, the preamble to an Act putting control of a long section of Ermine Street into the hands of the justices of Hertfordshire, Cambridgeshire and Huntingdonshire—in effect (as will be shown in a later chapter) England's first turnpike road—attributed the decay of the road to 'the great and many loads which are weekly drawn in waggons and the great trade in barley and malt that cometh to Ware.'

It was not until a century later, with the creation of the Stort Navigation in 1766, that the trade of Bishop's Stortford, hitherto relatively small, was greatly increased; it would no doubt have become even greater if the Navigation had been extended, as planned by the Duke of Bridgewater and surveyed by John Rennie, into the still incompletely tapped barely-growing area of Norfolk. Fumbling and inefficient management during the nineteenth century robbed both the Navigation Company and Bishop's Stortford of many anticipated benefits with the result that, though Bishop's Stortford's malt trade remained considerable, the town never achieved more than second place in the industry within the county.

It was with the invention in the eighteenth century of porter, which requires brown malt, that Hertfordshire barley combined with Hertfordshire skills to consolidate county supremacy. By the end of the century 5,000 quarters of malt were being delivered weekly to London from Ware alone. Maltsters were among the most influential members of turnpike trusts and river navigations, both lifelines of the malting industry; they were magistrates and members of parliament. Even the lesser men were prosperous. Robson's *Directory of Herts* (1838) lists 82 principal maltsters between Bishop's Stortford and Tring, Hoddesdon and Royston, 20 of them from Ware; how many others, of less importance, who combined malting with some other occupation were omitted it is impossible to determine. *A Guide to Hertford-shire* by Old Inhabitant in 1880 speaks of 'about eighty maltings' in Ware, describes the 'flourishing state' of Bishop's Stortford trade but, curiously enough, makes no mention of malting at Hertford, though there was still a good deal done there.

Then, fairly rapidly, came a decline, due in part at least to the re-moval to other centres of one London brewery after another, either in its new location taking their malt locally or setting up maltings of their own. But apart from this, the reasons for the decline are obscure. For all that many leading maltsters and malt factors were Quakers they were also men of business, to whom excise officers were thorns in the flesh; in 1786 an unpopular officer at Ware had been subjected to such a hostile demonstration that he allowed himself to panic and called out the military—for which he was dismissed. Many ingenious dodges for cheating the excise were known; the difficulty in account-ing in detail for the later decline in the industry is increased by the cryptic nature of many maltsters' records—it may be that they had the excise in mind when they made them. At any rate, by bankruptcy, intermarriage and amalgamation the two score or more of fairly large firms operating in east Hertfordshire in the mid-nineteenth century were steadily reduced to a handful; today there are no more than four —Harrington Page Ltd at Ware, French & Jupp Ltd at Stanstead Abbots, H. A. & D. Taylor Ltd at Sawbridgeworth and Bishop's Stortford, and Paine Ltd, brewers of St Neots, Hunts, at Baldock. An immense extension, erected by Harrington Page in 1966 to their already large, modern malting at Ware, and embodying new tech-niques, does not yet come within the purview of industrial archaeo-logy.

The traditional process of malting is simple yet subtle—its succes-sive stages are plain to anybody who has seen the interior (or even perhaps the exterior) of a malthouse. At one end of the building is the barley store, where the grain is allowed to lie for some time following delivery by the farmer. Just beyond the barley store is the cistern (though there may be more than one) in which the barley is steeped

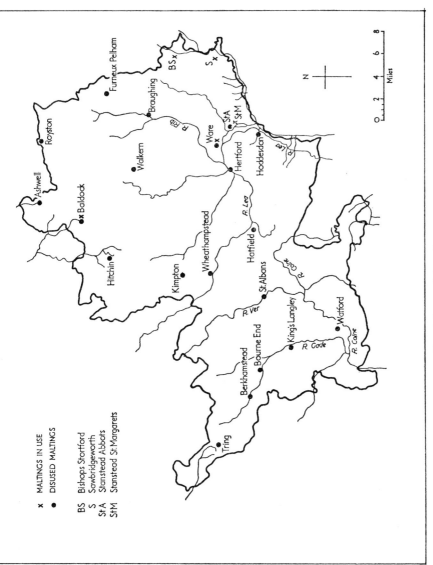

MALTINGS IN USE x
DISUSED MALTINGS ●

BS Bishops Stortford
S   Sawbridgeworth
StA Stanstead Abbots
StM Stanstead St.Margarets

Surviving malting sites

Furneux Pelham
Braughing
BS x
S x
Royston
Ashwell
Baldock x
Walkern
Ware x
StA x
StM
Hertford
Hoddesdon
R. Rib
R. Beane
Hitchin
Kimpton
Wheathampstead
Hatfield
R. Lea
St.Albans
R. Ver
Bourne End
King's Langley
Watford
Berkhamstead
R. Gade
R. Colne
R. Colne
Tring

N

0 2 4 6 8
Miles

for several days to allow it to swell; when the water has been drained off the barley is transferred to the couch, where it remains for a short time longer, its internal heat increasing somewhat. Beyond the couch lies the large malting floor, over which the grain is spread evenly to a depth not exceeding twelve inches. On the malting floor, and periodically turned over with large wooden shovels, it is allowed to germinate in a controlled temperature, germination being arrested at a desired point, so that the saccharine or farinaceous elements in the barley may, in brewing, be turned into alcohol by yeast in fermentation. This stage may last for between one and two weeks, depending upon the quality of the barley and the maltster's intentions; in judging the precise moment for its removal from the floor lies the subtlety of his craft. The germinated barley is then put into the adjoining kiln and dried into malt of the desired type, amber, brown, chocolate or black. At the extreme further end of the building is the malt store, where the newly kilned malt is sacked to await delivery to the brewer.

Malthouses are therefore long and, in general, low buildings, with the protruding dome of the kiln a good three-quarters of the way along the length—which, it must be emphasised, varies so greatly that no typical dimensions are worth giving; it may be a mere 70 ft or as long as 200 ft, depending, very roughly speaking, on the age of the building. Sometimes it happens that the barley store and malt store are in timber. Occasionally, adapting themselves to the restrictions of a site, they lie at right-angles to the main line. Malting floors, of which there may be two, three or possibly four, are always brick-walled, sometimes arcaded, though two small ones, at St Albans and King's Langley, are built of chequered brick and flint with brick quoins, the flint being characteristic of the chalk areas of the county (plate, page 18). The floors themselves are of wood, slate or, in a few instances, of tamped chalk (plate, page 18) in any case, giving a smooth surface on which the grain can germinate, the rate of germination being determined by the control of temperature through rows of windows, usually louvred but sometimes shuttered, on both sides of the floor. The floors, seldom more than 6 ft in height, are supported either by wooden pillars or more often by cast-iron columns; but the floor joists appear to be usually of timber.

At the base of the kiln is the furnace, fired in modern malthouses by oil or anthracite, formerly by coke (it is said that Abraham Darby first realised the advantages of coke as a fuel from his apprenticeship to a maltster), smoke and fumes being drawn off. In Hertfordshire hornbeam, one of the county's characteristic trees, was commonly used as fuel, giving great heat with no fume; indeed, a kiln operated by H. A. & D. Taylor at Sawbridgeworth still uses hornbeam faggots exclusively, of which immense stacks like haystacks are built close by.

Above the furnace the floors on which the germinated barley is spread are either, in modern malthouses, of porous tiles or, in older ones, of finely woven wire mesh—nineteenth-century Hertfordshire Directories sometimes list men describing themselves as wire weavers. There may be several of these kiln floors, one above the other. Finally, the dome of the kiln, circular or square and ensuring a strong upward draught, is usually of light wooden construction, plastered internally, and tiled or slated without, and surmounted by a cowl. Formerly cowls were almost always of the windbreaker type— tall, half-sugarloaf-shaped erections with fantail: old photographs of Ware or Bishop's Stortford show them in profusion. But today the type has been practically entirely replaced by the flat mushroom variety, possibly more efficient but certainly less picturesque. In some malthouses the cowl is merely a slatted and roofed extension of the dome.

In the figures on pages 38–9 are shown the section and ground-floor plan of a yellow-brick malthouse in Priory Street, Hertford, built about 1875 for Benjamin Young, a Hertford brewer who also owned several other malthouses in the town. Four floors in height, it is 111 ft overall by 40 ft wide, of which 76 ft are cistern, couch and malting floor, 35 ft kiln. The barley store is missing—probably Young stored his grain centrally and delivered it straight into the cistern. The malt store is at right-angles to the general line of the building, the site on which it stands being nearer square than rectangular. The

exterior of a more typical nineteenth-century malthouse at Stanstead
Abbots is illustrated on page 17, the barley store being at the right of
the picture and the original kiln replaced by a newer one. Both buildings still survive; the first is now a Housing Department depot of the
Hertford Corporation, the second, closed in 1966, has been bought
by the Lea Valley Regional Park Authority.

In all, Hertfordshire contains about 80 sites that are still being, or
in the past have been, used for malting—a precise figure is almost
impossible. Being considered of no particular architectural (though of
greater historical) interest, malthouses are extremely rarely listed for
preservation by the Ministry of Housing and the demand for concen-
tration of production within the industry has brought many into the
property market, their purchasers having no qualms about demolish-
ing them. Thus in 1964 there were in Ware 22 separate malting sites,
of which 7 were operating; 10 had been closed and some demolished
by 1968, and all the remainder except one were used for other purposes. At Bishop's Stortford in 1964 there were 17 malthouses, of
which all but 2 were used for other purposes (plate, page 17); at Baldock 7, of which 4 were used for other purposes; at Sawbridgeworth
2, of which the smaller was used for other purposes. Hertford has a
total of 9 sites, none now operating; and also disused are: Ashwell, 4;
St Albans, Tring and Wheathampstead, 2 each; Berkhamsted,
Bovingdon, Braughing, Furneux Pelham, Hatfield, Hitchin, Hoddesdon, Kimpton, King's Langley, Royston, Walkern and Watford, 1
each. Records of past malthouses, of which no trace now remains,
would at least double the total of surviving sites.

On the sites containing more than one malthouse, probably the
majority have the houses standing parallel, three, four, five or even
six alongside each other. At Sawbridgeworth, however, nine malthouses belonging to H. A. & D. Taylor Ltd are ranged end to end
over a total length of about 350 yd, with three additional houses in
the rear; but some of these are now used as the firm's garages or
workshops. Nevertheless their immense spread forms an imposing
picture in the lush quiet of the Stort valley. While the unencumbered

Page 35 (above) *Simpson Brewery, Baldock, demolished 1968;* (below) *Ashwell Brewery*

Page 36   (above) *Moor Mill,
Frogmore, St Albans;*
(below) *waterwheel,
Sopwell Mill, St Albans*

space of malting floors might be thought to facilitate the adaptation of disused malthouses to other purposes, their low height is a grave obstacle, especially since their fenestration is determined by that height; all the same, many malthouses which in less fortunate circumstances might well have been destroyed now serve as factories or workshops of all kinds, from light engineering to food processing, commercial or industrial showrooms or stores, part of a laundry at Kimpton, village or church halls at Ashwell and King's Langley, Boy Scout and other social centres. Several have been converted into dwelling houses; and one, at Bourne End, Bovingdon, was until about 1965 a boarding home for cats. Existing Hertfordshire malthouses, used and unused, are listed in the Gazetteer.

An interesting feature of two disused malthouses (one at Old Cross, Hertford, the other at Hitchin) is the sixteenth-century brick to be found in their base walls. Nothing to account for this brick has been discovered at the former; at Hitchin a malthouse on the site is known to have existed in the eighteenth century and a building of the same shape appears on the map accompanying Sir Henry Chauncy's *Historical Antiquities of Hertfordshire* (1700). At Tring a late eighteenth- and early nineteenth-century malthouse, not now in use, adjoins a small complex of buildings showing evidence of cruck construction. The site is known to have been occupied by maltsters since the seventeenth century, and it is open to the imagination that malting has been carried on here since, possibly, the Middle Ages.

Finally a brief record should be made of the destruction in 1966 of Hertfordshire's most intriguing malting site—Cannon Maltings, Ware. This consisted, firstly, of a central two-storey building in sixteenth-century brick, with a three-light, brick-mullioned window back and front and a dated brick, 'I.C. 1622'; and secondly, of two long wings of nineteenth-century brick, with a dated brick, 1836—but having in parts an inner skin of largely sixteenth-century brick as though, it may be, early buildings of some kind had been incorporated when the outer skin was built. The total length of wings and central building was about 120 yd. The malting history of the site

c

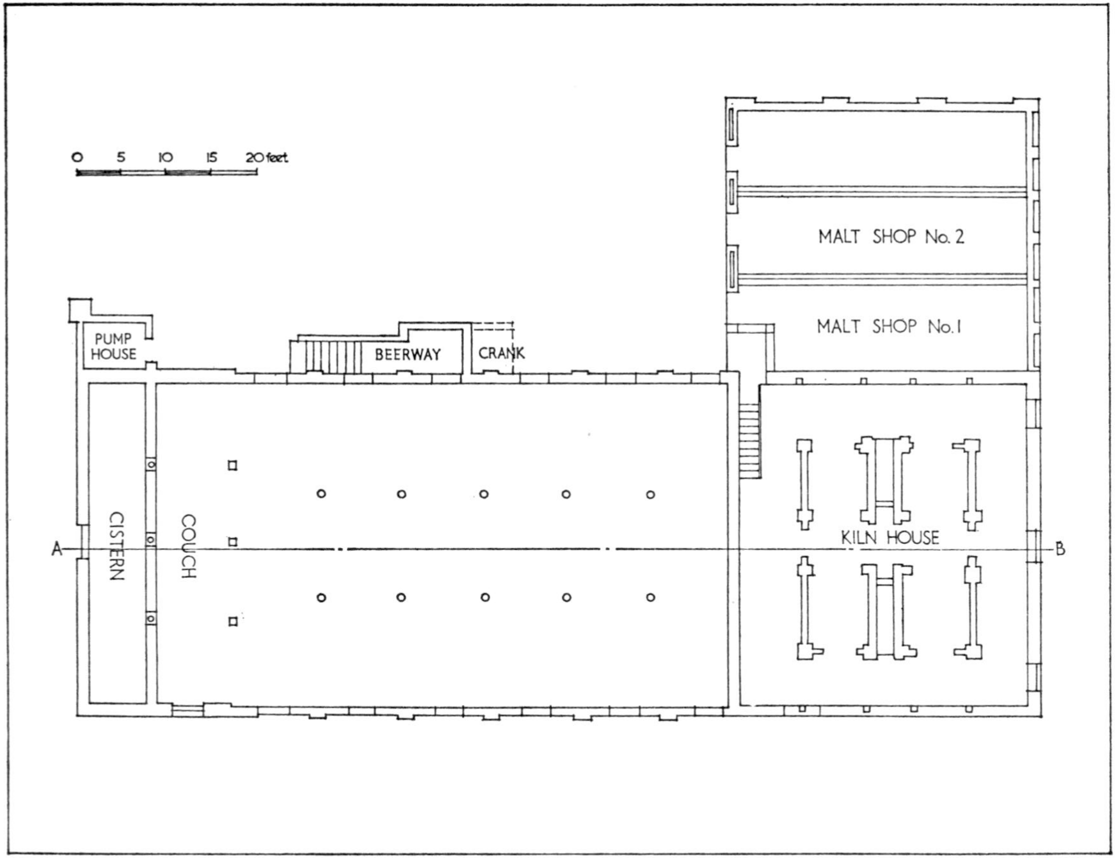

MALT SHOP No. 2

MALT SHOP No.1

KILN HOUSE

CRANK

BEERWAY

COUCH

PUMP
HOUSE

CISTERN

A

B

0 5 10 15 20 feet

Plan of a Hertford malting

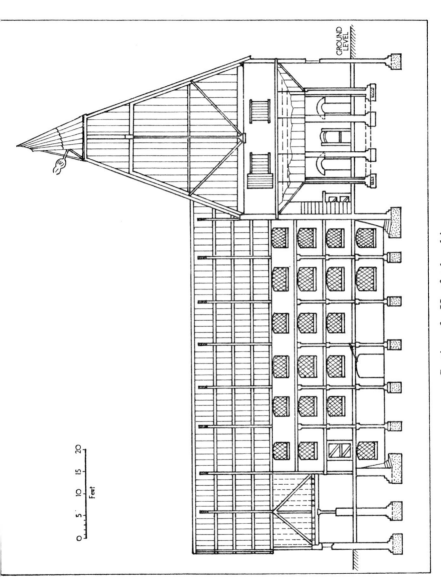

Section of a Hertford malting

0 5 10 15 20
Feet

GROUND LEVEL

could be traced back only to 1836; before that, nothing could be discovered and the brickwork of the five existing kilns offered no clue. The central building alone had been listed by the Ministry of Housing and Local Government, the true nature of the wings probably not being recognised. After operating until about 1959 it was used as a store for television sets until purchased by Ware Urban District Council. In spite of strong protests by the Ministry, the Hertfordshire County Planning Department and local historical and archaeological societies, the council, having already demolished parts of the unlisted wings, allowed the rest to become structurally unsound and completed demolition in connection with an area development scheme.

BREWING

There were, of course, brewers of ale in Hertfordshire, as elsewhere, from time immemorial, ale being a necessity of life until the advent of an assured pure water supply. By the fourteenth century manorial records in the county refer to 'common brewers'—brewers who brewed solely or chiefly for sale. With the fifteenth century came the introduction of hops and the evolution of ale into beer, which is longer-lived than ale; but only in 1504 does 'the Dutchman the bere bruer' receive mention in a Ware will and in 1514 a Welwyn innkeeper becomes a 'retaliator de la bere'. Much later in the century an Order in Council decreed, amongst other things, that alehouse keepers 'shall not brew in their own houses but take their drink from their brewer where it may so be had'—probably an attempt to ensure a proper strength to the customer, though also showing that brewers had become common in number as well as in name. But for all that, home brewing, especially in farming districts, continued for many centuries, if on a diminishing scale.

With the eighteenth-century invention of porter, which has a much longer storage life than beer, the brewing industry gradually came to assume the nature of big business. The term 'common brewer' persisted, however; it could be seen until 1967 over the door of a Hertford malthouse in the name of a late nineteenth-century owner, 'Percy Hargreaves Common Brewer'. Invention of new apparatus and improvement of old proceeded apace. Breweries were enlarged and new ones built; new men entered the industry. From about the middle of the century certain Hertfordshire brewers were following the fashion of buying up hitherto independently owned inns and alehouses, which they supplied exclusively with their own products—the tied house system. In pursuance of this policy large amounts of new capital were needed; in Hertfordshire they obtained this from such men as William Wilshere, lawyer of Hitchin, who in this way eventually became a partner in Whitbread's Brewery, London. By the early nineteenth century such Hertfordshire brewers as Lucas of Hitchin and Christie and Cathrow of Hoddesdon were acting as bankers in loans to other breweries. The tied house system received a further impetus by the passing in 1830 of the Beerhouse Act 'to permit the general sale of beer and cider in England', whereby any householder might obtain from the excise, on payment of two guineas, a licence to sell beer on or off the premises—a year or two later distinction was drawn between 'on' and 'off'. At that date, it may be added, beer did not come within the scope of temperance propaganda, which concentrated entirely on spirits and especially gin —in fact, the Beerhouse Act, which was not repealed until 1869, was at first regarded as a temperance measure. Today no more than a dozen free houses exist among Hertfordshire's 880 licensed premises and most of those appear to be mortgaged to a brewer.

In passing, it is interesting to note the number of big London brewers of the eighteenth and nineteenth centuries who chose to live in Hertfordshire; all except one chose the east side, the malting side, of the county. Henry Thrale, of the Anchor Brewery, Southwark, was a St Albans man whose name will be familiar to students of Dr Johnson. The Byde family, lords of the manor of Ware from 1661 to 1829, ran a brewery in Mile End, highly appreciated by Pepys. The Calverts, of whom it was jokingly said that they could walk down the whole eastern side of the county on their own land, were owners of a brewery in Thames Street which, under another name but still with a Calvert on the Board, suffered bomb damage in the Second World War. After 1781 Samson Hanbury, partner in Truman's Black Eagle Brewery, Spitalfields, lived at Thundridge, north of Ware; and at the turn of the eighteenth and nineteenth centuries Samuel Whitbread, though more closely associated with Bedfordshire, owned an estate at Essendon. In the nineteenth century Thomas Fowell Buxton, another partner in the Truman house, lived at Stanstead Abbots,[1] and for more than half of it the mansion of Theobalds, Cheshunt, was in the hands of the Meux family—it was Sir H. Bruce Meux who moved Temple Bar from London to Cheshunt in 1888.

There were others with closer county connections. John Charrington, who in 1766 acquired a brewery in Mile End Road and thus laid the foundations of the firm now known as Bass Charrington Ltd, was a son of a vicar of Aldenham, where he and many of his family are buried. William Booth of Stanstead Abbots, brother of Sir Felix Booth, distiller of London, is said in Hassell's *Picturesque Rides 30 Miles round the British Metropolis* (1817–18) to have had a distillery in the village, though nothing about it has been discovered. And Henry Gilbey, coach owner and driver of Bishop's Stortford, was father of Sir Walter Gilbey, equally well known with Booth as a distiller.

At the same time Hertfordshire had its own brewing fraternity— and a large one; in the middle of last century brewers were to be found operating in every town and in many villages as well. They included Lucas of Hitchin; Phillips of Royston; Simpson of Baldock; Steed and Oliver also of Baldock; Pryor of Hatfield; House of Harpenden; Christie and Cathrow of Hoddesdon; Peter McMullen, Baker, Medcalf and Nicholls, all of Hertford; Fordham of Ashwell; Hawkes of Bishop's Stortford; Locke and Smith of Berkhamsted;

---

[1] A private note (now in the Hertfordshire County Record Office) written in the 1870s by the Hertfordshire historian, John Edwin Cussans, says of Buxton's activities in Stanstead Abbots: 'He and his family gave away nothing beyond religious tracts and good advice. The one costs nothing and the other four pence a thousand. I could say much more of this pious brewer but I do not like to appear unkind.'

Lattimore of Wheathampstead; Dyson, Sedgwick and Healey, all of Watford; Groome of King's Langley; Salter of Rickmansworth; Holloway of Hemel Hempstead; Rayment of Furneux Pelham; Kingsley of Kimpton; Brown of Tring; Kinder, Kent and Searancke, all of St Albans—the Post Office *Directory of Herts*, 1855, lists a total of 44, not including some half-dozen who combined a little brewing with farming, butchering, coopering, keeping a post office and so on. The west Hertfordshire landowning and brewing family of Clutterbuck had their brewery at Stanmore in Middlesex.

Half a century previously Edward Fordham and Richard Flower (who married Fordham's daughter) had kept a brewery at Hertford —this Flower was a collateral ancestor of the Flower who later entered a brewery near Shaftesbury, Dorset, afterwards transferred to Stratford-upon-Avon. And in about 1799 James Ind, a small brewer of Baldock, had seen his brother, Edmund, move to Romford, Essex, where Edmund's son took as partners W. O. E. and G. Coope in 1845. Steadily, however, the process, common to nearly all industries in the approaching period, of closure, bankruptcy and amalgamation—brought about in many cases by the expanding service area offered by the big London houses—reduced the number of genuinely Hertfordshire brewers to a handful; their *coup de grâce* has been given only since the Second World War, McMullen Ltd of Hertford now being the sole survivors.

Here it may be interpolated that S. Wright & Co of Walkern, having developed from malting to brewing in 1870, ceased to make beer in 1924, confining themselves to cider. This too came to an end in 1955, and the firm now makes only soft drinks. From the eighteenth century or even earlier cider and perry were made in small quantities in the county but always, it would appear, for purely domestic consumption—G. A. Cooke's *Topographical and Statistical Description of the County of Hertford* (1830) says that no apples grown in Hertfordshire were used for cider making. So far as can be ascertained, Wright & Co is the only firm in the county ever to have made cider commercially, though there were two ginger beer makers in 1855.

Unlike malting, the processes of brewing are generally known and do not need to be repeated here. Moreover, in the very small handful of breweries still operating competition has, generally speaking, forced the replacement of practically all old apparatus by new, which is as yet of no interest to the industrial archaeologist. But breweries demolished in recent years must be recorded, since they will obviously find no place in the Gazetteer but include some notable sites.

Since 1965 there have been three demolitions in which the contents have been almost entirely scrapped or dispersed; in one case a few minor items went to the Hertford Museum. The most notable of these demolitions, made against a veritable storm of protest, was that of Simpson Brewery, Baldock, in 1968—a remarkably handsome late eighteenth- and early nineteenth-century yellow-brick building of three floors that dominated the wide and picturesque High Street of the town (plate, page 35). It was surmounted by a small turret containing a clock bearing no maker's name but dating from about 1760 and was flanked on each side by a mid-Georgian house that formed part of the brewery premises; luckily both houses have survived. Its equipment, dating in large part from the 1880s, was by Pontifex of London and David Roberts; and there was also, by Marshall and Sons, Gainsborough, a horizontal single cylinder steam engine of 1890. Originally built by John Izzard Pryor about 1780, the brewery was extended in 1811, passed in 1854 into the hands of two Yorkshiremen living in Cambridge, J. and J. G. Simpson. In the early 1960s the business (having in the meantime become a limited company with a Simpson no longer on the Board) was taken over by Greene King Ltd of Bury St Edmunds, Suffolk; the brewery was turned into a bottling store in 1965. In the following year it was bought by Baldock Urban District Council and its site is now an approach road to a new housing estate.

Not many miles off, at Ashwell, another brewery lies idle while its future is still in 1969 undecided. Built in 1839 by Edward Fordham, who had previously brewed on a smaller scale in the neighbourhood, it is a large complex of buildings in yellow brick with red-brick quoins and window heads (plate, page 35). Later additions do not disturb its homogeneity of style. At first operated by water power, it preserves its original wheel turned by a powerful underground spring, though it had, of course, long ago adopted steam. In 1953 Fordham sold to Greene King Ltd, under whom it became a bottling store; Greene King sold it in 1958 to Flowers Breweries Ltd, who were amalgamated with Whitbread Ltd in 1965.

A brief mention will suffice to cover the demolition at Watford of a large disused brewery run in the early nineteenth century by William Whittingstall, later by M. A. and F. J. Sedgwick Ltd, who were taken over by Benskin Ltd in 1924. Its only notable feature was an imposing Georgian house facing High Street, alongside which stood the brewery gateway crowned by an elaborate specimen of Victorian iron scrolled frame that at one time no doubt displayed the name of the firm. Total demolition took place in 1965 and 1966.

In some ways the most regrettable demolition of recent years took place in 1967 in connection with a road scheme—that of the small West Street Brewery, Hertford, owned by W. H. G. Nicholls. The Nicholls family had founded the brewery in 1855, rebuilding and re-equipping it in 1885. Virtually all the 1885 equipment—by George Adlem of Bristol, Pontifex of London and Lawrence of London—remained in use until the last; a survivor of the former building, and dating from about 1860, was a horizontal single-cylinder steam engine, having a cylinder of 2 ft by 1 ft diameter, wood straps metal bound, fly wheel of 5 ft 9 in diameter and stroke of 20 in. It bore no maker's name. There was also a No 1 Cornish boiler, 50 psi working pressure, hand fired, of 1885. Another interesting item was a bottling plant invented by D. Wickham of Ware about 1890 (six years later Wickham entered the general engineering industry, the firm, now a limited company, operating on an extensive scale over a wide field). The brewery office, it may be added, was in a house, dated 1719 and listed by the Ministry of Housing, once occupied by Richard Westall, RA, an eighteenth-century Hertford man. It is now (1969) in the course of restoration.

Five breweries of which the buildings are now used for other purposes are described in the Gazetteer; there remain three that are still operating, of which the most interesting is the small Furneux Pelham Brewery owned by Greene King Ltd.

It was built in 1860 by William Rayment, until that time principally a farmer who brewed as a sideline; in his hands and those of his sons it remained until 1895, when it passed to a relative, E. W. Lake. Lake and his sons continued to operate under the old Rayment name, turning it into a limited liability company in 1917. In 1931 it was sold to Greene King Ltd. Today it is managed by Commdr H. N. Lake.

A compactly built red-brick gravity brewery of three and two storeys, it is set at a crossroads in the most rural of surroundings adjoining a remote and picturesque village—a typical example of the small country brewery that has almost everywhere vanished, even though it is no longer independent of the big brewing concerns, as it would have been in the past. It still uses a copper by George Adlem of Bristol, 1895, and fermenting vessels by the same firm, 1880, as well as a mash tun by Briggs of Burton-on-Trent, about 1880. The tank in the tower is by Pontifex of London. Other equipment has been renewed.

At Watford the Cannon Brewery, owned by the Dyson family, was in existence in 1750; in 1868 it and the Dyson mansion adjoining were bought by Joseph Benskin. It was steadily enlarged by him and later by his widow and sons. Today, however, the mansion, now used as offices, is the sole object on this very extensive site of any interest to the industrial archaeologist; there is no part of the equipment that is not entirely up to date. In 1957 Messrs Benskin, though continuing to brew under their old name, became part of the immense organisation of Messrs Ind Coope Ltd—thus, after a century and a half, east Hertfordshire, in the ghost of Edmund Ind of Baldock, joined hands with the west.

In 1827 Peter McMullen was operating a small brewery in Railway Street, Hertford; later he moved to Mill Bridge. At the same date at Old Cross, just round the corner from Mill Bridge, there was a brewery owned by John Cater Adams, which was acquired in about 1852 by William Baker and named the Hope Brewery. In 1920 A. P. & H. McMullen Ltd took over Baker and the Hope brewery, though they did not complete occupation for six years. Baker's old house, with stone frontage to Old Cross, of two storeys with Doric columns supporting the upper, is now the brewery offices but most of the old Hope Brewery premises are now replaced by new.

Meanwhile, in 1891, Messrs McMullen had built in Hartham Lane, close to Old Cross, a large new red-brick brewery, with five floors surmounted by a tower containing a clock of 1829 by Moore & Son, Clerkenwell, restored by the same firm in 1891, and pinnacled by an elaborate ironwork crown and flag pole. Here, as at Watford, however, all equipment must necessarily be of the newest type, the only exception being a mash tun, still in use, of 1896.

MILLING

There is a public house at Codicote whose inn sign—now, alas, redesigned—used to depict a man emerging from a globe with a tankard of beer in one hand and a loaf of bread in the other. Beneath ran the legend: 'Help Me Through The World.' In the conjunction of bread and beer as the twin supporters of life the signpainter showed greater historical acumen than the *Victoria County History of Hertfordshire*, which in its section on industries, published in 1914, devotes some space to brewing but none at all to milling.

In 1855 the Post Office *Directory of Herts* listed 82 millers in the county (plus 7 millwrights); in 1864 Cassey's Directory listed 93. Even in 1902 there were 65. By 1937 the number had dropped to 19 and by 1965 to 14, of whom three worked only occasionally. Eight were milling flour, four dealt with animal foodstuffs and two (Royston and Standon) with soya products. This rapid decline may be accounted for generally by the advantages enjoyed by millers in large ports who are able to unload their imported grain direct from ship to silo, and more particularly in Hertfordshire by the effect of a steady fall in the water table, which put one water-powered mill after another out of action. While the county contains a number of mill buildings, it is a disappointing one from a more active point of view. Mills no longer at work are emptied of all gear.

The waterwheels, however, have not been removed in every case (plate, page 36). Three intermittently operating mills—at Frogmore, near St Albans, East Hyde near Wheathampstead, and Redbourn—are worked by water power alone. Ten disused mills still retain iron wheels, though no maker's name can be seen on any of them and the date of their installation is impossible to discover. The largest—an undershot wheel 22 ft in diameter and 6 ft in width—is in an eighteenth-century corn mill at Tring converted to a silk mill in 1824; the rest vary from 14 ft diameter and 8 ft width to 12 ft diameter and 6 ft width. There are, however, two, both overshot, which from their position cannot be measured exactly, of 12 ft diameter and between 12 ft and 14 ft width; they are pretty well all that remains of a mill at Hunton Bridge. Many other mills, of course, have a wheelhouse from which the wheel has been removed.

In addition, one wooden wheel still survives at Tonwell, near Ware. It is in fragmentary condition, 16 ft in diameter and 3 ft in width and with a few remaining iron floats. The private house into which the former mill has been transformed now serves as the judge's lodging during Hertford Assizes. There is a second and more complete one at Hunton Bridge, near Watford, previously used for pumping water to a mansion close by (see also page 95).

Virtually all mills built or rebuilt after about 1860 were, however, steam powered; some of the older ones turned from water to steam about 1875 and in the 1880s. Town Mill, Hertford, demolished in 1967, installed a horizontal turbine in 1895, and today at least six use electricity—among them Kingsbury Mill, St Albans, which was originally built for water, then adopted steam. Bridge Mill, Wheathampstead, turned straight from water to electricity.

Such large firms as J. & W. French of Ware, Bowman & Sons of

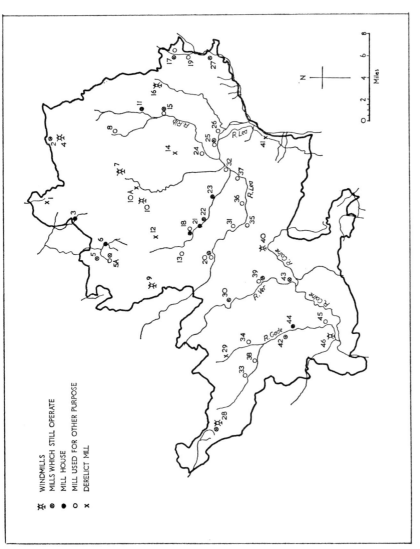

WINDMILLS

MILLS WHICH STILL OPERATE

MILL HOUSE

MILL USED FOR OTHER PURPOSE

DERELICT MILL

Windmill and watermill sites

Hitchin, or Heygate & Sons of New Mills, Tring, employ, of course, no equipment likely to interest the industrial archaeologist. Nor do the big mills of British Soya Products Ltd at Royston and Standon. It is among the smaller ones that interest must be sought.

In many respects the most interesting is Redbournbury Mill, in the valley of the river Ver south of Redbourn and about a quarter of a mile from Watling Street, A5. It is a small red-brick building of two floors and slated roof, about 50 ft square, on one wall of which is a dated brick, 1770. The adjoining millhouse is probably of about the same date. In the river is an iron undershot wheel, very difficult of access but about 8 ft in width and probably 16 ft in diameter. In 1840 the mill was operated by Edward Hawkins; today it is worked, though only occasionally, by his lineal descendant, Miss I. Hawkins. Its entire equipment appears to belong to the early nineteenth century, of wood construction often handsomely turned.

At East Hyde near Wheathampstead is a large L-shaped mill and store, of two floors partly weatherboarded, built in 1835. The store is now empty. Shortly before 1890 the whole premises came into the possession of Benjamin Cole, who had previously worked a mill at Codicote; his grandson, Mr S. W. Cole, who breeds cattle on the adjacent farm, still works the mill occasionally for animal foodstuffs. This he does single-handed, allowing none of his men inside the building. It has an iron undershot wheel of 14 ft diameter and 8 ft 6 in width, the race running through the middle of the mill. A good deal of his equipment dates from about 1880, possibly earlier, including a dressing machine by S. Howes, Silver Creek, New York, whose agents are stated on it to be Howes & Wells, Mark Lane, London.

Another mill of some interest is Kingsbury Mill, St Albans, with a pleasant eighteenth-century frontage in red brick (part of which was probably the miller's house) but earlier, timber-built, rear portions. Since it lies alongside the Ver on the site of the Saxon successor to Roman Verulamium, the antiquity of milling at this spot is not open to much doubt; now the mill produces animal foodstuffs, most

of its gear being modern and its iron undershot wheel, 12 ft in diameter and 6 ft in width, lying idle. A curiosity is its sack hoist on the
top floor, in which the wheel of the hoist rises to the brake instead of
the brake descending to the wheel.

One other mill deserves to be singled out, though not for anything
it contains. In the early 1950s Broxbourne Mill on the river Lea, then
used by an engineering firm, was largely destroyed by fire. The burnt
building appears to have been of early or mid-nineteenth-century
date. What the fire mercifully spared, however, was a stretch of wall
built of flat sixteenth-century brick, with a tiny single-light, stone-
cased window, and also what was probably the miller's house of two
floors, a possibly late seventeenth- or early eighteenth-century cottage construction, in one wall of which is a delightful Regency Gothic
window of two lights. So far as can be ascertained no other mill in
Hertfordshire contains sixteenth-century brick. Of some interest too
is the millhouse at Mill Green, Hatfield, which has a dated brick, I.B
1762. I.B was Joseph Bigg, whose descendants continued to work
there for four generations. It ceased milling in 1911.

In a fair number of villages small mills have been demolished,
leaving only the millhouse, occasionally with the race beneath it, as a
private residence. But Picott's End Mill, Hemel Hempstead, itself a
handsome three-floor, weatherboarded structure on a brick base and
probably dating from the eighteenth century, has attached to it a
Georgian millhouse, 1783, of three floors, large sash windows, brick
cornice and central doorway flanked by Doric pillars and with a
radiating fanlight. At Frogmore, near St Albans, Moor Mill (plate,
page 36) also has an eighteenth-century millhouse attached, but of
two floors only, with rusticated stone quoins and modillion cornice.
Moor Mill itself contains two wheels, both undershot, one (occasionally worked) of 10 ft 6 in diameter and 6 ft wide, the other (no longer
worked) of 10 ft 6 in diameter and 7 ft 6 in width. The building is,
however, attacked by death watch beetle and its future must lament-
ably be regarded with anxiety. Noke Mill, Great Gaddesden, has a
modest seventeenth-century millhouse close by, timber-framed with

overhang and now in a poor state. The mill dates from mid-nineteenth century; some years ago the entire site was threatened with
demolition, a threat now happily diverted.

Up to about twenty years ago Hertfordshire could claim a dozen or
more windmills; now there are eight. The county's only post mill—
at Cromer, near Ardeley—closed down about 1930 and thereafter
rapidly deteriorated; its timbers fell apart and it suffered from both
dry rot and furniture beetle. Partly because of its uniqueness of type
in the county, partly because it formed a conspicuous landmark,
widespread concern was felt lest, as seemed inevitable, it should soon
fall down altogether; and in 1967 and 1968, by grants from the
Hertfordshire County Council and the Hertfordshire Building Preservation Trust, and by private subscriptions, its fabric has been
restored (plate, page 53). Sails will be added as funds become available
and its old gear will still be in place.[1] But no operational use is envisaged for it; it is likely to remain a landmark but nothing more. The
work was carried out under the direction of the Hertfordshire
County Planning Department and the Hertfordshire Building
Preservation Trust.

Another windmill—a smock mill—deserving similar consideration
(though less likely to receive it) is that at Little Hadham, built in 1777
and working until 1929 but now in very sorry condition (plate, page
53). Hertfordshire's remaining six windmills are all tower mills; one of
them, at Breachwood Green, King's Walden, can scarcely survive
much longer. All the tower mills are empty of gear and at present in
indifferent condition; of them one is being converted into a dwelling
house, another into a workshop. It is interesting to add that both
these, their sails having been blown off in gales, were at one time
worked by steam. At Weston, Lannock Mill bears the inscription
'R Xtey 1860', having been erected by Richard Christey in that year.

[1] Sails were placed in position in 1969.

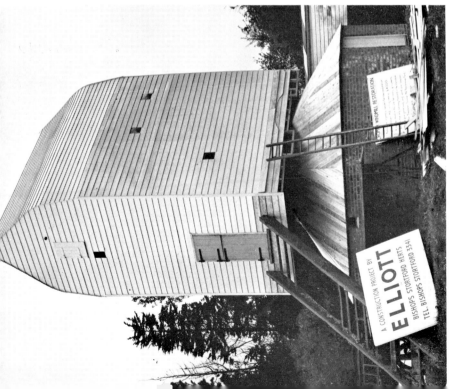

Page 53   (left) Cromer, Ardeley, post mill during restoration in 1968; (right) Little Hadham smock mill

Page 54 (above) 'Wet end' of a
Tidcombe papermaking machine at
Frogmore, Hemel Hempstead;
(below) Caslon proofing press, Apsley
Mill, Hemel Hempstead

PAPERMAKING

Hertfordshire has two claims to interest where papermaking is concerned—here thin white paper was made in England at a very early date, and here were developed the machines upon which the modern industry is based.

By 1494 John Tate, son of a Lord Mayor of London, owned a paper mill at Hertford—there is still a Paper Mill Mead at the north end of the town. Tate, whose watermark was an eight-pointed star within two concentric circles, the larger about 1¼ in diameter, made paper for Caxton and Wynkin de Worde and received several 're-wards' from Henry VII on visits to Hertford Castle. However, when he died in 1507, though he left estates elsewhere to his eldest son and to a friend 'as much white paper or other paper as shall extend to the sum of 26s 8d . . . out of my paper mill at Hertford', the mill itself was directed to be sold 'to most advantage'—which, it was suggested later, meant that it had been faced by too keen a foreign competition for its continuance to be acceptable to his heirs.

What happened to the mill is unknown—indeed, nothing further about papermaking is heard for more than a century. Then, in 1649, Sopwell Mill, St Albans, on the river Ver, is described as a paper mill, only to revert to corn milling by 1691. Meanwhile paper was being made at Hatfield, in a mill on the river Lea, by 1672; this mill had a long life, closing only about 1835. Next came a paper mill at Standon, on the river Rib; it was working by 1713 but in 1855 was turned into a sawmill.

The eighteenth century saw the establishment of a number of small paper mills, mostly converted corn mills, in the west of the county, along the rivers Chess, Colne and Bulbourne, with others on the Ver and the Lea. Those on the Chess, with their approximate dates of working, were: Sarratt (1744–c 1871); Solesbridge, Chorleywood (1746–1888); Mill End, Rickmansworth (1755–1905); Scots Bridge, Rickmansworth (1757–1881); and Loudwater, Chorleywood (1757–

D

1885). On the Colne were Batchworth, Rickmansworth (1755–1886); Hamper, Watford (1776–1908); and Bushey (1788–c 1820). On the Bulbourne there was a mill at Bourne End about which nothing is known except that it operated between 1768 and 1794. On the Ver Redbourn mill worked from 1753 to c 1796 and on the Lea Pickford mill, near Wheathampstead, from 1775 to 1849. The four survivors of these mills—Scots Bridge, Solesbridge, Hamper and Pickford— are described in the Gazetteer. Thus early papermaking was—and here it fits appropriately into the Hertfordshire pattern—an entirely rural industry.

At first paper was made in sheets and to a large extent by hand in all these mills; in some of them no change appears to have been made throughout the working life of the mill. On the river Gade in 1763 there was also a mill at Two Waters, near Hemel Hempstead, taken over about 1792 by Henry Fourdrinier and his partners and run by them for a quarter of a century. By 1803 they had also acquired a second mill close by, at Frogmore, which had operated as a paper mill since 1774. And in these mills, though chiefly at Frogmore, two Fourdrinier brothers, Henry and Sealy, revolutionised the industry by producing paper not in sheets but in an endless roll that could be cut as required.

Hitherto all paper had been made from rags soaked in water, beaten to a pulp by water-powered hammers, bound together under pressure to a paper-like consistency and then dried—the complete process might take anything up to a week or two. Under the Fourdriniers the early stages of soaking and pulping remained substantially the same; but in 1802 they acquired the English patent rights of a French invention, made a few years previously but the exploitation of which the aftermath of the Revolution had prevented in its own country. They called in the services of the engineer, Bryan Donkin, and by 1804 had produced a machine capable of operational use at Frogmore. It was, as described in the *Victoria County History of Hertfordshire*, 'essentially consisting of an endless web of woven wire cloth, moving forward slowly over a series of small rollers in a hori-

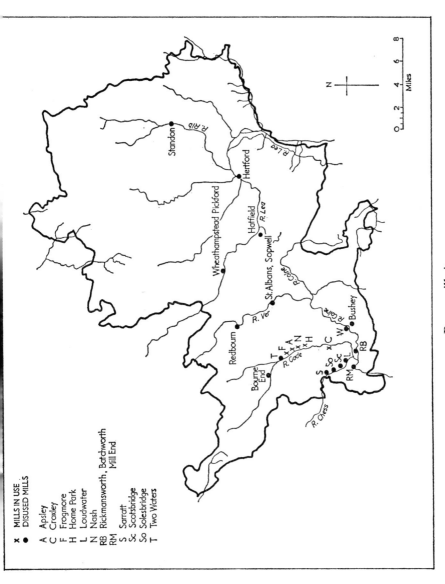

MILLS IN USE
DISUSED MILLS

A Apsley
C Croxley
F Frogmore
H Home Park
L Loudwater
N Nash
RB Rickmansworth, Batchworth, Mill End
RM
S Sarratt
Sc Scotsbridge
So Solesbridge
T Two Waters

Paper mill sites

zontal plane, the paper pulp flowing on to one end of the level part of
the wire, water being drained off from it as the wire moved forward
and the partly drained pulp, after consolidation between two rollers,
being drawn away from the surface of the wire as a continuous web
of paper'. By compression between further rollers the paper could be
dried at once, thus enormously shortening the time factor. First experiments had made paper only a few inches wide and of inconsider-
able length; within a few years the wire cloth, or gauze, was 33 ft 6 in
long and 4 ft 10 in wide, making a paper roll of any desired length.
But the Fourdrinier brothers became involved in litigation and were
bankrupt by 1810, though they did not leave Two Waters and Frogmore until 1817—by which time, however, thirteen machines had
been built for papermakers in other parts of the British Isles.

An incidental problem of all papermakers until the introduction of
alternative raw materials in the nineteenth century was the supply of
sufficient quantities of rags to meet their needs. What amounted to a
minor industry developed out of rag collection both locally in Hertfordshire and from London. On delivery at the mill the rags were
sorted and cut up, chiefly by women and children, who, to judge
from Quarter Sessions records, were by no means averse from steal-
ing them. Whether the wages paid were lower than in other local
employments is not clear; but over and above theft, Quarter Sessions
had from time to time to deal with threats of the withdrawal of
labour, at that time an illegal proceeding. Some, however, seem to
have arisen—as they did elsewhere—from the introduction of new
machinery.

In the years before the Fourdriniers became bankrupt a neigh-
bouring mill, Apsley Mill, Hemel Hempstead, was bought by John
Dickinson. Apsley had been making paper by the old method since
1774 and for some years Dickinson, a young London stationer, had
been a customer there, as well of the Fourdriniers. In 1807 he had
already taken out patents for making cannon cartridge paper and for a
papercutting machine; in 1809, the year of his purchase of Apsley, he
patented a cylinder papermaking machine—in effect, a modification

of the Fourdrinier machine but taking up much less floor space, which is still used for certain types of work. Two years later he bought Nash Mills, Abbot's Langley, a short mile below Apsley on the river Gade; on his marriage in 1811 he installed himself in the millhouse at Nash Mills, a pleasant Regency building now used as board room and offices. Business acumen and inventive energy reaped steady rewards; in 1826 he built Home Park Mills in King's Langley and in 1830 Croxley Mills, Rickmansworth, also on the Gade. In addition he leased the mills at Two Waters and Frogmore and also a mill at Batchworth, Rickmansworth; these three the firm continued to hold until it became a limited liability company in 1886, when the leases were surrendered.

To this expansion the times were favourable. Though Hertfordshire as a whole remained virtually untouched by the Industrial Revolution, business enterprise demanded more and more paper for a multitude of purposes. Government requirements proliferated. The introduction of the penny post in 1840 gave further encouragement and so did the repeal of the Newspaper Duty Act in 1855. But it was Dickinson himself to whom primary credit must be accorded. Having manufactured great quantities of cartridge paper during and after the Napoleonic wars, as the years passed he made the silk-thread paper for Exchequer Bonds and other Government documents, the first Mulready envelopes, paper for early issues of postage stamps, as well as stationery, art paper, card and many other varieties. It was he who introduced the silk thread as a protection against forgery and devised a method of extracting the iron dust that had previously tended to discolour white paper. In all he took out some twenty patents. In short, he was that admirable person, a man in harmony with his times and equipped to take advantage of them. Scientific study of the bases of papermaking led to his election as FRS and, for hobby, he was a keen astronomer, having an observatory attached to Abbot's Hill, Abbot's Langley, to which he moved from his original home at Nash Mills.

After John Dickinson's death in 1869 the firm continued to be held largely by his family, becoming, as previously stated, a limited liability company in 1886; in 1966 it merged with E. S. & A. Robinson Ltd, when it was making such well-known writing papers as Basildon Bond, Lion Brand, Croxley Brand and Queen's Velvet. What, then, about the new group's Hertfordshire mills?

The Dickinson administrative centre is at Apsley Mill. Even in 1819 it was described by John Hassell in his *Tour of the Grand Junction Canal* as having been enlarged and 'rather resembling a village than a manufactory'; today it covers more than 30 acres, including, as well as the transmogrified eighteenth-century millhouse, a number of buildings dating from 1887 and later. Though it turned from water power to steam in 1815, the old mill race from the Grand Union Canal (which here runs alongside the river Gade), conduited and built over, still flows through the middle of the site; two undershot waterwheels were removed in 1923. It builds much of its own machinery in its own engineering department, but still employs a master blacksmith working at a forge, made by Allday and Onions, Birmingham in 1870, now with power-operated draught in place of its original hand bellows; he still uses tools bearing the Dickinson factory marks from 1820 onwards. One of the current anxieties of the firm concerns his eventual replacement, master blacksmiths being nowadays among the rarest of men.

In the midst of vast masses of the latest machine designs it is curious to find a hand-operated envelope machine made at the Dickinson works, though not a Dickinson invention, about 1860 and also a hand-operated proofing press by H. C. Caslon, Chiswell Street, London, of elaborate early Victorian (even if not earlier) design, both in use (plate, page 54). It is interesting too to come across models of a beam engine and other types, constructed on the premises about 1900, from which today's apprentices become conversant with yesterday's technology.

Except for the millhouse that Dickinson made his home in 1811, Nash Mills was completely rebuilt after a fire in 1813 and has been again rebuilt in recent years. Originally water powered, it turned to steam in 1824. Modern too is Home Park Mills; it was steam powered from the first, though an undershot wheel, latterly used for pumping water to the cistern in the tower, was not removed until 1960. At Rickmansworth, Croxley Mills retain only a portion of the original Egyptian-style frontage, now enclosed in new building.

Complete modernisation of equipment is a foregone conclusion in so large an enterprise as that of Messrs Dickinson; at Frogmore Mills, operated since 1890 by the British Paper Co Ltd, it is perhaps appropriate that memories of the Fourdriniers should to some extent be revived. The present buildings were, however, not erected until 1863 and are run by steam power, with two large coal-burning boilers, about 1900, by H. & T. Dawes of Netherton, Dudley. It contains, apart from more modern equipment, a Fourdrinier-type papermaking machine with drying cylinders by George Tidcombe of Watford (see also page 151), dating from before 1886 (plate, page 54); another Fourdrinier-type machine and drying cylinders by Redfern Smith & Law of Bury, 1891; and a third by J. Milne & Son of Edinburgh, 1896. All these machines are in current use. Also in use are two sheetcutting machines by G. Bertram & Co, of Edinburgh, one of which was exhibited at the Crystal Palace Exhibition of 1872, the other dating from 1875.

CHAPTER THREE

Miscellaneous Industries

SOME of Hertfordshire's minor and temporary industries of the eighteenth century—calico printing at Hertingfordbury, optical glass grinding at Tewin, diamond polishing at St Albans—have already been mentioned in Chapter One. During the next century a number of small industrial concerns, including a few iron and brass founders, established themselves in the towns of south Hertfordshire, chiefly in the Lea valley; but they were short-lived, little or nothing is known of their history and no relic of them survives. Remembered for longer than most was the mid-century Abbey Ironworks at Waltham Cross, making the iron frames for old-fashioned mangles; it was founded by a man named Cole who also had the wit to open near the works a beerhouse, which he called the Moulders' Arms. The works closed after only a few years but the Moulders' Arms continued until recently.

There were, however, a few industries of wider scope and greater importance to the county. Whether or not they survive today, they demand closer attention.

SILK THROWING

Up to the eighteenth century the weaving of cloth for local use was carried on in many towns and villages, as it was in most other counties, but the industry declined as the century progressed. Later there arose, particularly at Tring, a small canvas-weaving industry—indeed for much of the nineteenth century Tring had four canvas-weaving mills, the last working as late as about 1920. But on a bolder scale was the silk-throwing industry that is first heard of in Watford near the end of the eighteenth century and is continued today in the nylon manufacturing of the Kayser-Bondor Hosiery Mills Ltd at Baldock. Incidentally, there is a silkworm farm at Salisbury Hall, Shenley.

The reason for the appearance of the silk industry in the county can only be guessed at. Nearness to the great market and port of London no doubt contributed. Spitalfields, not far away, had a long silk-weaving tradition based on Huguenot labour. Were Hertfordshire expertise in straw plaiting or Buckinghamshire and Bedfordshire skill in lacemaking appreciable factors—or the existence of canvas weaving at Tring? To make matters more uncertain, the qualifications of most of the founders of the Hertfordshire industry remain obscure.

In 1771 the Sessions records of the Liberty of St Albans note an appeal against an assessment for poor rate by Edward Crutchley and John London, 'occupiers of a silk mill at Watford'. Their mill was almost certainly Rookery Mill on the Colne at the lower end of the town. The *Universal British Directory* (1792) speaks of a 'Mr Paumier'—probably Pierre Paumier, member of a second generation Huguenot family in England—as operating three silk mills there; he had been in the town since at least 1780, when his daughter Margaret married William Harty, though at what date he succeeded Crutchley and London is unknown. The three mills were Rookery, worked by water power, and two smaller ones, one said to have been in Red Lion Yard on the site of the present-day covered market, the other at Clarendon Road corner, both worked by horses. Highway rate lists for 1836 and 1837, now in the Watford Public Library, give four mills, all in different occupations but without a clue to their whereabouts. Robson's *Directory of Herts* (1838) records only two: Rookery and one occupied by Thomas Toppin or Tuppin. The other two had vanished and Toppin himself vanishes thereafter.

By 1806 Paumier had given place at Rookery Mill to his son-in-law Harty, about whom little is known except that, according to Hassell's *Tour of the Grand Junction Canal*, he ran 'the celebrated silk mills'; and by 1826 to Thomas Rock Shute, born at Sydenham, Kent in 1802 and thus a very young man for his position. Whether Shute's family had any previous connection with the silk industry has not been discovered; at any rate, he evidently made a success at Watford, since he continued there until his death in 1881. Then the mill closed down, becoming in turn a steam laundry and a piano factory; today, after a destructive fire, its remains (with recent extensions) house several small firms of engineers and joiners.

It was Harty of Rookery Mill who established a silk mill, described in 1806 as newly built, at Rickmansworth; since it was situated on High Street (a present-day mineral water factory may be part of it) steam power was probably employed from the first. An entry in the Rickmansworth Vestry minutes of 1807 shows that Harty manned the mill, partially at least, with pauper children, a source of cheap labour tapped by all other silk mill owners in Hertfordshire. At first he took only six from the Workhouse; but to judge from knowledge of other mills, it seems probable that the number quickly increased— and here it may be interpolated that all estimates of individual silk mill manpower should be regarded as the merest approximations; the figure that may be most usefully borne in mind is the aggregate given in Robson's *Directory of Herts* (1838): 'At St Albans, Watford, Rickmansworth and Tring about 1,200 persons of both sexes are employed in throwing and winding silk.' The 1891 Census, on the other hand, records only 160 males and 396 females so engaged.

Like his predecessor at Watford, Thomas Rock Shute appears at Rickmansworth; he was still there at the time of the 1851 Census. By 1855 it may be that the mill had been acquired by his former manager, James Lawton, a Cheshire man, though this is not certain. In 1874 it was bought by Coventry Hart but closed fifteen years later, in 1889, when it was occupied by James Hart—'situated', say the sale particulars published in the *Watford Observer* (21 September), 'close to the high road and with a right of way thereto through double entrance gates. It comprises a substantial brick-built factory about 74 ft long and 30 ft wide, containing 3 well lighted floors, an engine and boiler house and chimney shaft, also a double brick-built cottage containing 7 rooms and a garden.'

Silk mill sites

The Abbey Mill at St Albans on the river Ver, lineal descendant of the corn mill of the medieval Abbey, was a long eighteenth-century building of three floors, liberally fenestrated, with the river (containing the wheel) running through the middle; adjoining at right-angles to its west end stood the millhouse, a rambling affair dating from the seventeenth century, which was added to in Regency days. In 1804, mill and house were acquired by John Woollam and became a silk mill and Woollam's residence. Nothing has been discovered of Woollam's antecedents or of his qualifications as a silk man; whatever they were, it could be said in Brayley and Britton's *Beauties of England and Wales* (1806) that 'this manufacture . . . promises to become flourishing, and a new mill is now fitting up near the former one'. Although two large buildings (one with what appears originally to have been a second wheel), described in C. H. Ashdown's *St Albans Historical and Picturesque* (1893) as 'modern', make the earlier disposition of the site difficult to follow, there still exists a red-brick, two-storey erection, dated 1810; alongside and badly bonded into it is a three-storey house of about the same date, designated on an Ordnance Survey town plan of 1880 as 'school'. Was this school a philanthropic gesture on the part of the Woollam family or strictly vocational in its teaching? For at least two generations of Woollams worked Abbey Mill, using partly water power, partly steam. In 1806 Brayley and Britton wrote that the mill machinery, which filled three rooms, 'is very ingeniously contrived; some of it is constructed on a new and much improved principle'. Nothing is known of its equipment when, in 1906, it was sold to J. Maygrove & Co of London, who continued to operate there until 1938 and to own it until about 1955. Then its new owners, Faith Craft Studios Ltd, demolished the old mill and leased most of the remaining buildings to other firms. The millhouse is in separate ownership and occupation.

Having established himself at St Albans, John Woollam expanded to Hatfield, where by 1818 he was employing pauper children. The second edition (1849) of Lewis's *Topographical Dictionary* implies, however, that some adults worked there as well. Very soon afterwards the mill, which Lewis says was steam powered, seems to have closed down. In place of it, in the late 1850s, a steam-powered mill was built by the Woollams at Redbourn, facing the common. This of course recruited local labour; but there survives a surgeon's certificate under the Factories Regulation Act, 1844, requiring children to be at least eleven years old before working there. Whether these children were paupers is uncertain. The Redbourn mill was continued by Maygrove and, like Abbey Mill, closed only in 1938. Its present owners, Brooke Bond Tea Ltd, now display the large bronze bell, made by J. Warner & Sons, London, in 1858, formerly used to summon the eleven-year-olds and their elders to labour.

Before coming to the last large silk mill to be established in Hertfordshire the short-lived experiment of John Ransom of Hitchin may be briefly noted. Ransom ran Grove Mill at Hitchin as a corn mill; it appears to have been rebuilt in 1814. In Pigot's *Directory of Herts* (1826) however, he is listed as a silk throwster. It seems likely that he continued corn milling at the same time; in 1838 Robson's *Directory of Herts* records that for silk throwing the mill 'has hitherto been but partially worked'. And in Pigot's edition of the following year Ransom is listed as miller only.

In the nineteenth century Tring had two silk mills; but of one in Frogmore Street, which closed in 1860, only the name of its last owner, Thomas Evans of Crayford, Kent, is known. Yet the name is intriguing; what, if any, was his connection with David Evans & Co of London, later of Dartford, Kent, who for more than half a century ran the much larger and longer-lived mill in Brook Street?

The Brook Street mill (plate, page 71) was established in 1824 by William Kay a year after his purchase of the manor of Tring. After operating it himself for four years he leased it to David Evans & Co, then of Cheapside, London. Kay was a Cumberland man by birth, apparently the son of a yeoman farmer of Wigton from whom he inherited the farm and £100. His family had widespread connections and many different interests; but the extent of his connection with the silk industry—or with other Kays in the textile industry in Lancashire and Cheshire—is unknown. On his death in 1838 William bequeathed the mill, with the rest of the manor of Tring, to his descendants, in whose hands it remained until they sold the manor to the first Lord Rothschild in 1872. In 1887 Evans's lease appears to have terminated; thereafter the mill continued operating under the first Lord Rothschild, became a company (N. M. Rothschild & Co) under the second, and finally closed in 1898. After various vicissitudes it now houses the R.M.R. Engineering Co Ltd.

In its pre-silk days Brook Street mill had been a water-powered corn mill; Messrs Evans quickly supplemented water power with steam power. E. C. Osborne's *London and Birmingham Railway Guide* (1840) which contains much information on the mill, says that 'there is a steam engine of twenty-five horse power . . . appropriately called Venus and was constructed at the manufactory of Peel Williams and Peel, Manchester. There is also water power equal to that of sixteen horses'—the wheel being fed from a large pond and spring outside the mill manager's house. Messrs Evans appear also to have been determined builders, as can be seen from a general view of the present site. Nothing of the old mill is identifiable; instead there are two main brick-built blocks, one 150 ft by 35 ft, originally of five floors but now of three, the other, of two floors, 100 ft by 35 ft. At their junction are the boiler house and the enclosed iron waterwheel, the latter, no longer used, being 22 ft in diameter and 6 ft wide. There is also a number of miscellaneous buildings and ample stabling. In addition the firm ran a smaller factory in Akeman Street and another, manned by pauper labour, at Aylesbury, Bucks, having 40 looms in 1830 and 70 in 1865.

As in the Hertfordshire industry generally, 'its silk', says Osborne, 'is imported from Italy, China and Bengal in the skeins and undergoes in the mill the various operations called winding, doubling, spinning etc. . . . The work, when it has undergone the various mill operations, is forwarded to the London and Manchester markets and some is sent to Coventry to supply the ribbon weavers there.'

Of all Hertfordshire mills Tring is, thanks to Osborne, the only one in which a glimpse can be had of the contemporary conditions. At the time he wrote it was, according to him, 'capable of employing 500 pairs of hands, consisting of 40 men, 140 women and 320 children. . . . The superintendent gets a pound a week; the general run of the men's wages is between twelve and fifteen shillings a week; the average of women's wages is five shillings and sixpence a week, and of children three shillings; the time of the latter is regulated by Act of Parliament to ten hours a day, the adults to twelve.'

Whether from benevolence or business foresight, 'the proprietors of the mill pay Mr Dewsbury, surgeon, £20 a year for inspecting the persons employed in the mill to insure cleanliness and freedom from disease'. Disease, however, did not include ague—and Tring, comments Osborne, 'is seldom or never without ague'. Nor was Dewsbury concerned with ensuring healthy living conditions. It is true that at least some of the 320 children were lodged in a long single-storey building facing the mill and now used as offices, where they were supervised by matrons; yet Osborne thinks fit to comment:

> The temperature of the mill is about 60 degrees and the people employed, though pallid enough, present rather a better aspect on the whole than those in the mills of Manchester, but still they are far from appearing to be a healthy and happy people; the children in particular appear doleful and dejected; some of them have a precocity of visage that is absolutely startling. They are taught to sing hymns as they work, and when a stranger comes, to affect a semblance of sanctity and sing out with unusual energy; it would perhaps be a wise reform to do away with this schooling of hypocrisy; and peradventure it might be found that music of a livelier character would have a more stimulating and beneficial influence upon the nerves and general health of these poor innocents.

One poor innocent commiserated by Osborne was Gerald Massey, of some popularity in his day as the Chartist poet but now largely forgotten except as the prototype of Felix Holt in George Eliot's novel of that name. The son of penniless parents, he entered the mill in 1836 at the age of eight; he is said to have worked from 5 am to 6.30 pm, his weekly wages varying from 9d to 1s 3d. After he had been there a few years a fire seems to have ended his employment; for many hours, wrote Samuel Smiles in *Eliza Cook's Journal* (1851) 'he stood in the wind and sleet and mud rejoicing in the conflagration that liberated him. . . . He then turned to straw plaiting.'

But before we too turn to straw plaiting it remains to be noted that, while the mills at St Albans and Redbourn were still at work in the twentieth century, two new firms established themselves in Hertfordshire, both about 1928. They were the Ballington Hosiery Co Ltd, later Ballito Hosiery Mills Ltd, at St Albans, who closed in 1967, and the Fully Fashioned Hosiery Co Ltd, now Kayser-Bondor Ltd, at Baldock. Kayser-Bondor still occupy a large factory originally built by a firm of photographic chemists, who went bankrupt before its completion.

STRAW PLAITING AND STRAW HAT MAKING

An incidental but by no means unimportant by-product of Hertfordshire agriculture was wheat straw which, when cleansed and cut into short lengths, could be plaited into patterned 'twist' for making straw hats, bonnets and other articles of apparel. Whether straw plaiting, which was carried on mainly as a secondary occupation by village women, can rightly be called an industry is a moot point, though straw hat making raises less difficulty; but straw plaiting played so significant a part in the lives of the Hertfordshire labouring classes over fully two centuries that note of it can scarcely be omitted.

Shakespeare's several references to hats of straw show that the making of them, and by implication the prior making of twist, was known in England, though not necessarily in Hertfordshire, in his day. But in 1664 Pepys's womenfolk donned straw hats 'much worn in this country' (that is, district) at Hatfield. By the end of the seventeenth century Hemel Hempstead, Tring, Hitchin and other towns sold straw plait in their markets and contemporary documents show straw plaiting as an established occupation in such villages as Great Gaddesden, Flamstead and Redbourn—nearly all, it will be noted, on the west side of the county, where the weaker straw grown on chalk was more pliable than the stronger straw produced on the

Page 71 (above) *Brook Street Mill, Tring, formerly a silk mill;* (below) *fulling stocks at Horns Mill, Hertford*

Page 72 (above) *1880 copper still, herb distillery, Hitchin;* (below) *grinding mill, old terra cotta works, Broxbourne*

clay soils. In his *Tour of the Whole Island of Great Britain* (1724) Defoe comments on the spread of straw plaiting from Hertfordshire where it was already widespread, into Bedfordshire. As the eighteenth century progressed there came a fashion in straw for an immense variety of articles and straw headgear, particularly for ladies, became the very height of fashion. Almost every Hertfordshire village woman took to occupying herself with straw plaiting and straw hat makers multiplied in the towns, though the two biggest hat centres, Dunstable and Luton, lay just over the county boundary in Bedfordshire. The heyday came with the Napoleonic wars, when blockade and high import duties excluded foreign and especially Italian plait. The Society of Arts and the Society for Bettering the Conditions of the Poor were active in encouraging improved strains of English straw used for plaiting, and in other directions as well. At a time when the average Hertfordshire agricultural wage was between 10s and 12s a week, straw plaiting wives could earn appreciably more than their husbands and children's contributions to the family income were considerable. 'The farmers complain of it as doing mischief', declares Arthur Young in his *General View of the Agriculture of Hertfordshire* (1804), 'for it makes the poor saucy and no servants can be procured or any field work done where this manufacture establishes itself.' But he adds that 'good earnings are a most happy circumstance, which I wish to see universal', again emphasising that 'straw plaiting is of very great use to the poor and has had considerable effect in keeping down rates, which must be far more burthensome without it'.

Though the coming of peace after 1815 reduced (and later abolished) import duties, impetus and high craftsmanship carried the Hertfordshire industry through the nineteenth century with only a slow decline. Indeed, it was for long difficult to see any decline at all. For at least the first half of the century earnings remained reasonably high. All over the county village women were seldom met without fingers busy among the straws that, when plaited, draped in long lines of twist over their arms. In many villages plait schools sprang up, usually conducted by elderly dames (occasionally illiterate) who

E

taught plaiting to youngsters of the tenderest years; if a little reading or figuring were included in the so-called curriculum they were by way of make-weight only. As mentioned in an earlier chapter, when Queen Victoria passed through Hitchin in 1851 on her way to Balmoral the station was decorated with straw plait in celebration of the event— and of the paramount local industry.

But slowly foreign competition finally triumphed, particularly from China and Japan, which could produce an article cheaper than, though inferior to, any within Hertfordshire's powers. Earnings decreased; alternative employments for women gradually opened up. Of the 283 men and 3,133 women recorded in the 1891 Census as being employed full-time in straw plaiting or straw hat making it is safe to say that the majority worked at the latter, in Luton as well as in Hertfordshire.

Perhaps in the end it was a change of fashion that strengthened if it did not administer the death blow; Edward VII is said to have been the last monarch to wear a straw boater and one school after another, in which a boater decorated with the school colours had been part of the uniform, abandoned these hats. With changes in feminine headgear demand fell off heavily; what remained was abundantly satisfied by foreign plait. By the outbreak of the First World War only a handful of straw plaiters survived throughout Hertfordshire. It can confidently be said that today there is not one. All that remains are museum exhibits of the simple tools of their craft.

Around straw plaiting two ancillary occupations grew up. The first was straw dealing—the buying of unthreshed wheat straw from farmers and the preparing of it for the plaiters to whom it was sold. The second was plait dealing, which had arisen by the end of the eighteenth century and consisted simply of buying the finished twist from plaiters and selling it, with guarantee of quality and quantity, to hat makers. It sometimes happened that the village grocer was also the local plait dealer, paying in domestic goods for the twist he bought —an obvious advantage to the plaiter, who was thereby saved a journey to a market perhaps some miles away, but fraught with equally unpleasant possibilities to her if the grocer were of the Chestertonian variety. Many plaiters preferred to sell their plait direct, combining sale and home marketing in a day's jaunt, for all that it robbed them of a day's work. Nevertheless, plait dealing so far prospered as to warrant the formation in the mid-nineteenth century of an association which lasted for some thirty years, when the increasing importation of foreign plait, over which members had no control, led to its falling into abeyance.

St Albans, the centre of the straw hat making industry in Hertfordshire, was always subservient to Luton not many miles away. Like plaiting, hat making was principally a women's occupation, men being for the most part confined to blocking, stiffening and packing—a good many of these men worked at home on one process only, selling the half-finished product to St Albans or Luton factories. Thus Kelly's Directory for 1882 lists in St Albans 40 straw hat manufacturers; of these, two or three were branches of firms from London or elsewhere, with large local premises, and half a dozen or more of true Hertfordshire origin, also with premises; the rest—say about 30 in all—were home workers. Earlier directories list straw bonnet makers; usually these were women in large villages or small towns who combined straw work with general millinery, occasionally men who undertook straw work as a sideline—like the straw bonnet maker at Hertford in 1855 who also ran a post office. By the end of the century most of these village workers were selling their products to Luton rather than to St Albans. As to the St Albans industry, in the words of the *Victoria County History* (1914):

The smaller factories as a rule only do part of the work of hat-making, usually the sewing. The larger firms sew, block, stiffen and trim hats ready for the market, the work being done partly by indoor and partly by outside labour. They also buy and finish work already sewn. . . . Gentlemen's hats are the principal articles made at St Albans, but the small factors . . . sew ladies' hats for manufacturers at Luton. . . . Many of the St Albans manufacturers block and trim a quantity of imported goods. In St Albans alone over eleven hundred persons are employed in the trade at the height of the season.

But with the decline in the wearing of straw boaters and the increasing domination of foreign plait (which, of course, affected both centres) St Albans trade gradually drifted away to Luton. Some firms, however, survived the First World War and continued into the late 1920s. Today the St Albans industry is remembered by one or two buildings, now used for other purposes, that were formerly straw hat factories; but there is nothing about them to indicate as much. At Hertford the industry is recalled only by the faint remnants of an inscription on the wall of a house facing Port Hill, 'Hertford Straw Hat & Bonnet Manufactory'.

FULLING

Memories of medieval days, when Hertfordshire was a sheep-rearing county with Hitchin as its chief wool market, are stirred by the very rare discovery in Horns Mill, Hertford, of a battery of five fulling stocks in regular industrial use, even though that use is not the original one.

Fulling was the cleansing and felting of newly woven and therefore loose-textured cloth. The earliest reference to the process in Hertfordshire is the village name, Walkern, the place where cloth was 'walked'—that is, trampled by foot to expel its oily residues and to shrink and bind it into felt. Mechanical substitutes for walking had emerged by the end of the twelfth century and in the middle of the thirteenth the Abbot of St Albans converted a number of water-powered corn mills on the Abbey estates into fulling mills. Mills were converted or built by lay lords of the manor in widely separated places, from Gilston, Standon and Braughing to Berkhamsted and Hemel Hempstead; local records from other parts of the county, revealing the presence of fullers in their respective localities, suggest more. How long these mills lasted can very seldom be traced; all had vanished by the end of the seventeenth century. But not quite always the name: a rather more detailed history of what is still called the Fulling Mill at Codicote is of great interest.

The Codicote fulling mill, previously a Domesday water corn mill, stands on the river Mimram just at the boundary of Codicote and Welwyn. Codicote was a St Albans manor; but it is from Welwyn that the first reference comes, in the name of Robert Strayler, in the Welwyn Rectory court rolls of 1287. 'Strayle', according to the *New English Dictionary*, was coarse blanketing used for bed-clothes. In 1352 John Strayler was a Welwyn innkeeper and in the sixteenth century there was a Welwyn family called Glascot alias Fuller. At Codicote John le Fuller died in the Black Death of 1348. In 1427, the will of a Codicote woman, Alice Forager, left to her daughter 'a piece of cloth that is at the fuller's'. The last reference to a fulling mill in the village is in the Codicote parish registers, which record the burial of Thomas Martin, a fuller, in 1601. Twenty-five years later Quarter Sessions books call it Bilgrave Mill, its ancient name, without indicating its use; but by 1740 the minute book of the Welwyn Turnpike Trust shows it definitely to have been a corn mill again. Yet although it has not fulled for at least 200, maybe 350 years, and was, moreover, rebuilt at about the end of the eighteenth century, it is today invariably known as the Fulling Mill and the road leading to it is officially named Fulling Mill Lane.

Fulling stocks were in normal use all over England until the invention in 1823 of the rotary fuller and its substitution during the next forty or so years for the older type. The stocks at Horns Mill, Hertford, were almost certainly purchased in 1891 from a woollen mill in the west or north of England, where they were to be replaced by rotaries.

It was in 1891 that Webb & Co first came to Hertford from Surrey, occupying a mill that had been used for corn milling, then for rape cake manufacture. Rebuilt in 1858, it was at first water powered but was soon converted partly, later wholly, to steam; in 1918 the original steam engine gave way to the present two-cylinder marine one. Messrs Webb were leatherdressers and since 1915 have specialised in chamois leather fur-lined gloves for cold climates. The fulling stocks are now used to impregnate lamb and sheep skins ('fleshes') with cod liver oil in the production of chamois leather—and occasionally of buckskin for Lifeguardsmen's breeches.

The fulling stocks are illustrated in the photograph on page 71. A full description of them, by Mr E. J. Connell, appeared in *Hertfordshire Past and Present*, No 6, 1966. Mr Connell writes:

> The main material used is heavy timber and cast iron plates and pillars. The feet are 4 ft 6 in long and 1 ft across, with a maximum thickness of 18 in stepping down at the lower end. In two of the sets [the stocks are erected in pairs] these 'soles', are faced with steel to reduce wear. Each foot is fastened by wedges to a shaft 10 in by 3 in and is pivoted to fall through a curve of 6 ft 6 in outside radius. The ends of these shafts are bolted through trunnion plates which pivot on an axle supported centrally by a cast iron pillar. The pillar is set leaning outwards from the base and is obviously designed so that the feet would turn a broad cloth with the least attention. . . . The boxes are reinforced by cast iron plates at the sides and at the base of the column. The base curves up to match the radius of the feet as they fall.
>
> The long wooden shafts carrying the feet project about a foot beyond them and are soled with an iron plate where they are lifted by the tappets. Each pair of feet is worked by 6 tappets, 3 on each side of a cast iron wheel 6 ft in diameter. As the stocks are set in pairs, there is a second wheel 3 ft away joined by a massive axle to the first. The tappets lift each foot alternately three times in one revolution, the vertical lift being 2 ft 6 in, so that the feet fall by gravity as the wheel rotates. In order that the foot can be held in the raised position without stopping the millwheel there is a long wooden lever—a stang. This rests on a bar running across the top of the box frame and can be pushed into a slot at the top of the foot when the tappet has lifted it to the highest point. Before the tappet moves on to let the foot drop, the stang is pulled down to lift the beam clear. The handle of the stang passes through a metal plate with sides cut in the slot to hold the stang in the raised or lowered position. The operator is protected from the rotating tappet wheels by a fence round the pits in which they run, with axles only a foot below floor level.

These Hertford stocks, it will be noted, are of the same design and very much the same dimensions as those formerly at Cam, Gloucestershire, described in the *Journal of Industrial Archaeology*, Vol 1, No 1 (1964) and may be by the same maker, probably William Kilburn of Leeds, though even an approximate date, other than between 1810 and about 1850, cannot be ascribed to them. They appear to have been overhauled, either in or before 1891, by Hoxham & Brown of Huddersfield.

Until about 1955 a Hitchin firm of leatherdressers operated fulling stocks on their premises. Then, unfortunately, they were broken up without, so far as can be discovered, any note being taken of them.

HERBS, TERRA COTTA AND EXPLOSIVES

At Hitchin also, but still in full production, is the herb distillery of William Ransom & Son Ltd, founded in 1846 by a member of a long-established Quaker family of the town—it was another member, John Ransom, who twenty years earlier had experimented in silk throwing at Grove Mill. William acquired a number of old buildings lying back from Bancroft, the principal street of Hitchin, and approached through the high gateway of a seventeenth-century timber-framed house, now occupied by the firm's caretaker; some of these buildings were destroyed by fire in about 1960 and have been replaced but the rest are still in use. In his time nearly all the herbs for distilling, including great quantities of locally grown lavender for making lavender water, came from Hertfordshire; today they arrive from all over the world. It may be added that William's grandson, Mr Richard Francis Ransom, is the present chairman of the company, and that his great-grandson is also in the business.

Much of the equipment in current use is up to a century old, though it cannot be dated with certainty. Some stoneware tincture jars, about 3 ft high and marked Z.811.T, are by Doulton & Co, Lambeth, who before 1858 had been Doulton & Watts. Messrs Ransom had a large Doulton & Watts jar of similar design until 1967, when it was apparently scrapped without its interest being recognised. A series of evaporators—handsome copper-lined pans about 5 ft in diameter in cast-iron jackets on iron-legged pedestals—are by James Shears & Son, London, who became Bennett Son & Shears in 1892; a purely aesthetic judgment might place these evaporators a good deal earlier than that. Bennett Son & Shears are also the makers of a large digestor 7 ft in diameter and 10 ft high. No maker's name can be found on the firm's stills (plate, page 72) and percolators but their appearance would seem to show them as belonging to the nineteenth century. A cast-iron press about 10 ft in height belongs probably to the early part of that century.

In the year before Ransom opened at Hitchin, James Pulham, a local plasterer and builder, established at Broxbourne a terra cotta and artificial stone works, building for the purpose, in brick liberally decorated with terra cotta accessories, a mock Elizabethan factory, to which a Victorian dwelling house was afterwards added. Taking swift advantage of the prevalent rage for church restoration, Pulham's work can be seen (though less easily recognised, perhaps) not only in a great many Hertfordshire churches but as far afield as St Mary Redcliffe, Bristol. His fame extending, he was engaged to construct rock gardens at Sandringham; later his son was to build rock gardens for the Royal Horticultural Society at Wisley, Surrey, and part of the Mappin Terraces at the Regent's Park Zoo for the Royal Zoological Society. Rock gardens and other work by Pulham & Son can be seen on the Leas at Folkestone, at St Anne's-on-Sea, Lancashire, at Blackpool and on St Stephen's Green, Dublin. When cremation first became fashionable the firm turned its attention to cinerary urns and was among the first to make artificial stone bird baths. By the end of the nineteenth century it held a Royal Warrant of Appointment to the Prince of Wales, which was continued when he became Edward VII and renewed by George V, for whom much work was done in the gardens at Buckingham Palace and at Windsor.

Under Pulham's grandson, however, the firm came to an end at about the period of the Second World War. Its site, which included a large horse-operated grinding mill for pulverising stone before moulding, and also several kilns for making terra cotta, was bought by the Hoddesdon Urban District Council. Some of the premises have been demolished and converted into a car park; but some remain, though in a shabby condition, and so, at the time of writing, do the grinding mill and one kiln. Great efforts are being made locally to secure the mill's permanent preservation; but since the decision rests with the Urban District Council, its future cannot be regarded with certainty (plate, page 72).

At Barwick Ford (Standon) on the river Rib, a few miles north of Ware, are the remains of an explosives factory established in 1889 by the Smokeless Powder Company and designed by the company's engineer, Ernest Spon. The site is about 1,500 ft square, with the Rib on its eastern side and a lane on its western; it is roughly bisected by a wet ditch from the Rib. Much of it today is rough grazing ground; but there remain five stone-built magazines, eleven blast mounds, a factory building now occupied by a firm of specialist motor body-builders, the former laboratory, now a private house, and two other houses, one the dwelling of the former works manager.

By 1899 the factory had been taken over by the Schultz Gun-powder Co, a German firm employing nearly all German workers, many of whom were housed on the site. In 1914 they were, of course, interned and the firm transferred to the Government for the manu-facture of Sabulite, a high explosive composed of 78 per cent ammonium nitrate, 8 per cent TNT and 14 per cent calcium salicide, used to fill hand grenades and in peacetime for blasting. At the end of the war the factory returned to private hands as the Sabulite Co Ltd, later becoming the Sabulite Snap Co making explosives for crackers —it may be interpolated that a Reliance Snap Co has been similarly engaged at Bishop's Stortford for nearly forty years, though no con-nection between the two firms has been traced. In 1946, however, the sale of the large estate of which Barwick site formed part led to its purchase by one of the partners in Sabulite Snap Company, Mr H. E. Sears. He closed the works, resold the site in lots and con-tinued to live in one of the houses until his death in 1965.

Since 1933 Messrs Brock Ltd, makers of Crystal Palace fireworks, have operated on a large scale at Hemel Hempstead.

LONDON COAL DUTY BOUNDARY MARKERS

Hertfordshire is one of five counties containing a series of monuments which, though not in their employment of industrial use, are in themselves of sufficient interest as specimens of Victorian iron founders' and stonemasons' work to warrant brief mention. They are the boundary markers of the area covered by the City of London Coal and Wine Duties.

An Act of 1667 and another three years later, chiefly concerned with the rebuilding of London after the Great Fire, empowered the City Corporation to levy a duty on coal and wine entering it from other areas. By an Act of 1851 (14 and 15 Vic c 146) boundary markers were set up alongside railways, waterways and roads at points 20 miles from the General Post Office in St Martin's-le-Grand; each marker bore the city arms and the citation of the Act. Ten years later another Act (24 and 25 Vic c 42) substituted the Metropolitan Police District boundary and previously erected markers were, where necessary, transferred to their new sites, their inscriptions being amended accordingly, in most cases by a new plate with the 1861 citation bolted over the old. Coal and wine duties were repealed by the London Coal Duties Abolition Act, 1889, but the markers were left untouched. In 1961 the City Corporation put into excellent order all markers listed for them by the local authority in whose area they stood; it still maintains them. A total of about 250 markers encircles London, of which 44 are in Hertfordshire (see Appendix One).

Markers in Hertfordshire are of the four types illustrated in Fig 7. Two types are found alongside railways. The first is a graceful stone obelisk between 12 ft and 14 ft high on a base about 4 ft square; one stands erect on the east side of the main line out of King's Cross, between Potters Bar and Brookmans Park stations; one at Wormley and one at Watford lie broken on or very near their original sites. The second railway type is a cast-iron pyramid on a square base,

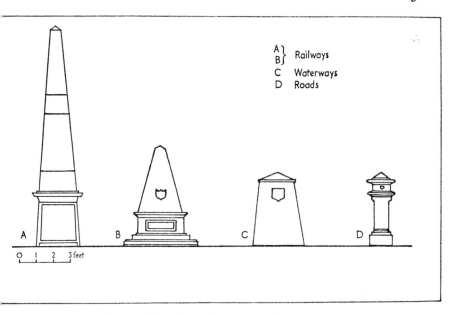

A } Railways
B }
C Waterways
D Roads

Types of London coal duty boundary markers

about 5 ft 6 in in height, made by the Falkirk Iron Co Ltd; examples are to be seen at Radlett and Oxhey, with a third only a few yards over the county boundary at Northwood, in Middlesex.

A third type is seen alongside the Lea Navigation at Wormley and the Grand Union Canal at Rickmansworth—a slightly tapered stone obelisk about 3 ft square at the base and 4 ft high. But by far the commonest type, of which there are 36 examples in the county, is alongside roads. It consists of a cast-iron column with bevelled corners, surmounted by a cap bearing the city arms and resting on a square base with the name of the maker, Henry Grissell, Regents Canal Ironworks, London, and sometimes a date. When out of the ground it stands about 4 ft 6 in high but when installed on its allotted site varies greatly, one or two markers, probably as the result of later road repairs, now being less than 2 ft above ground level.

This type can be traced right across the south of Hertfordshire, from Wormley, through Cheshunt, Hatfield, Northaw, Potters Bar, North Mymms, Colney Heath, London Colney, Shenley, Radlett, Watford, Bushey and Oxhey to Rickmansworth.

CHAPTER FOUR

Public Services: Gas and Water

GAS

In 1822 the St Albans Corporation gave permission to Joseph Hedley & Co 'to break up the road and to lay gas pipes'. Two years later Hedley had done nothing; whereupon the corporation entered into correspondence with the General Gas Light Company. What the outcome of this may have been is not clear; but in 1826 a gas company for the town was formed 'by private speculation' and in due course the principal streets were lit, the corporation supplying the lamps, the company the gas. The houses of subscribers were also lit of course, and presumably so were at least some public buildings, though it was not until 1849 that the corporation ordered gas to replace candles in the police station. Three years later the private company gave way to a joint stock company.

Although St Albans may take credit for being the first locality in Hertfordshire to contemplate gas lighting, it was in practical fact forestalled by Hertford, where the International Gas Co built works in 1825—'it was calculated', says the second edition of Cooke's *Topographical and Statistical Description of the County of Hertford* (1830), 'that the service pipes would be laid down, lamps etc erected, in the course of November following, when the splendid illumination afforded by these means would put Hertford upon a footing equal to any town of its extent in the three kingdoms.' By that time gas illumination (though not heating or power) had for long, of course, been a topic of widespread interest—in London, Pall Mall and Westminster Bridge had been gas lit for ten or more years and Whitehall for nearly as long, with other streets following suit. In Hertfordshire too the example of St Albans and Hertford was steadily followed. Ware established a Gas Co in 1830, Hemel Hempstead, Hitchin,

Bishop's Stortford and Watford in 1834, Baldock in 1837, Hoddesdon in 1847 and Berkhamsted in 1849. In the 1850s came Waltham Cross, Royston, Stevenage, Buntingford, Hatfield, Rickmansworth and Tring; and in the 1860s certain large villages were not to be outdone —Harpenden, Boxmoor, King's Langley, Much Hadham, Barkway, Hunton Bridge, Redbourn and Stanstead Abbots.

It was in 1860 also that at Welwyn gas was first supplied not by a company but by a local landowner, G. E. Dering of Lockleys. A brief history of this personal enterprise is interesting. Welwyn streets had been lit after a fashion—that is, by a piece of cotton wick floating in oil—under the joint control of the Welwyn Turnpike Trust and the Welwyn Vestry as early as 1820, a notably early date in a village for so communal a service. Dering was a man of great inventive ability in many fields, who could not have failed to earn a place in technological history had circumstances compelled him to greater activity in exploiting his patented inventions; his establishment of a gas works (one fragment of which still remains) was in line both with his own inclinations and with his genuine concern for the village. Mains were soon extended to Codicote, Digswell and Tewin Water; but after a time, for all that the vestry in 1864 imposed a 'voluntary rate at sixpence' on property for street lighting, enthusiasm waned and money became harder and harder to obtain. In 1876 the *Hertfordshire Almanack* had to report that 'the streets have not been lighted since 1873 owing to a difficulty in raising the required subscription'; though the difficulty appears to have been overcome a few years afterwards, even in 1901 lighting took place only between Michaelmas Day and Lady Day. By that date Dering had leased the works to two Welwyn operators; on his death in 1911 they appear to have bought them under the title of the Welwyn, Knebworth and District Gas Co. Fourteen years later the company amalgamated with the Hatfield Gas Co as the Welwyn and Hatfield Gas Co Ltd; this in its turn amalgamated with the Watford and St Albans Gas Co Ltd in 1933, who closed the Welwyn works entirely.

This process of the amalgamation of small and often struggling companies by larger and more prosperous ones—the main feature of the early twentieth century—was due partly to massive technical developments, partly to the wide use of gas for heat and power as well as for lighting, not less to the demands of a steadily increasing Hertfordshire population. In 1929 the Tottenham and District Gas Co Ltd took over Waltham and Cheshunt, in 1932 Hoddesdon, Ware and Hertford, in 1936 Hitchin and Stevenage. In 1929 Bishop's Stortford Gas Co became the Bishop's Stortford and Epping Gas Co Ltd and during the 1930s all the surviving small companies in the west of the county were absorbed by the Watford and St Albans Gas Co Ltd, which had itself been formed by the amalgamation of the two individual companies in 1930. Under nationalisation in 1949 Hertfordshire now lies within the area of the Eastern Gas Board, with the exception of Tring, which is in the Southern Gas Board. St Albans, Watford and Hitchin still manufacture coal gas, while preparing themselves to deal with natural gas in the years ahead; some other former works are now holder stations but several have been demolished.

Of these three manufacturing centres, Watford is the most rewarding to the industrial archaeologist, in that it has a column-guided, 2-lift, cast-iron gas holder of 1903, while the present-day retort house encloses a former one containing twelve horizontal retorts 26 ft long, originally installed in 1880 though more than once renewed since then; formerly hand-fed, they have been mechanically fed since 1909. The offices of the first Watford Gas Co, in a typical 1834 building of yellow brick, with stone window and door heads and slate roof, is still the local office of the Eastern Gas Board and there are other nineteenth-century buildings now used as stores. St Albans has been entirely modernised except for a 1901 column-guided, 3-lift, wrought-iron gas holder of 570,000 cu ft capacity by Samuel Cutler & Co, London. The Hitchin centre was transferred to a new site as recently as the 1960s.

The oldest gas holder in the county—a column-guided, 2-lift, wrought-iron one—is at Waltham Cross, Cheshunt; it was installed in 1880. Another, at Bishop's Stortford, by R. J. Dempster & Sons, London, dates from about 1890. There are several more column-guided holders—at Hemel Hempstead, Harpenden, Royston and Ware—of which it is possible to date only that at Hemel Hempstead (1904).

At Hertford the retort house and what was probably a large coal store, with 24 in walls, of the 1825 company are still used, though Hertford ceased making gas in 1958 and is now a holder station and coke distribution centre. At Harpenden, Waltham Cross and Ware (all holder stations) the former retort houses are now let to commercial firms. As at Hemel Hempstead, Hertford still has its engineer's house adjoining the works, built probably in the 1870s; at Royston, though the rest of the works (except a gas holder) have been demolished, two engineer's houses, one dated 1872, the other probably about 1890, still stand.

A small works of unusual origin is at Stevenage, where a Gas Company was formed in 1855 and production ceased in 1936. Here the first retort house is a nineteenth-century red-brick wing of the old seventeenth-century timber-framed workhouse, which was used as offices. This retort house was, however, superseded in 1903 by a much larger newly built one for horizontal retorts on an adjacent site; it is now a store of the Eastern Gas Board but all the older buildings are in private hands.

It may here be mentioned that the first electricity works in the county were opened in 1900 by the North Metropolitan Electric Power and Distribution Co Ltd at Hertford and Barnet. Watford Urban District Council also had its own electricity works by 1902. Privately generated electricity was, however, no new thing; it had been introduced into, for instance, Hatfield House in 1881. In the words of Lord David Cecil, 'the installation was very dangerous. Apart from the risk of shocks, the naked wires on the Gallery ceiling were apt to break into flame. The family sitting beneath nonchalantly threw up cushions to put the fire out and then went on with their conversation.'

Page 89 (left) *1890 gas engine, Hitchin;* (right) *gas standard and pump, Hemel Hempstead*

Page 90   (above) *Hunton Bridge wooden waterwheel*; (below) *donkey wheel near Harpenden*

Two cast-iron curiosities at Hemel Hempstead—one outside Box-moor Hall, the other in High Street—may appropriately serve as a link between this section and the next (plate, page 89). Both are fitted with electric light; but the bulbs are enclosed in typical nineteenth-century gas lanterns, with spiked ribs and were, until 1967, sur-mounted by a ventilating pinnacle shaped like a flame. Running up the outside of each structure is an iron pipe from ground to lantern, no doubt installed when gas was added. For in the first instance these structures, about 10 ft high and handsomely designed, were erected as water pumps with drinking fountains attached; the handle of that outside Boxmoor Hall is now missing. Both were the work of a local craftsman, John Cranstone, whose successors became the Hemel Hempstead Engineering Co Ltd; one was erected in 1835 'to com-memorate the third centenary of the first printing of the English Bible', the other 'by public subscription. J. Cross, Bailiff' in 1848. Of less interest is a pump surmounted by a lamp standard at Hexton; though the pump dates from 1846 the lamp standard is modern.

WATER

It might be regarded as a cause for sardonic amusement that, whereas the novelty of gas lighting was quick to catch public imagina-tion, the far more vital problem of assuring a pure water supply attracted much less interest. In bygone centuries a few private bene-factors, like Marmaduke Rawdon of Hoddesdon in 1630, had canal-ised a supply of running water to their immediate localities; nearly everywhere, in town and villages alike, ponds and wells sufficed for the needs of a much smaller population than today's—a reference in the corporation minutes of St Albans to a waterworks in 1696 is an unexplained mystery. By the end of the eighteenth century a few pumps and wells appear to have been under communal control or at least supervision; but they were not many. Into the wells seeped the sewage that had periodically been deposited in a near-by river or spread as manure over the fields—indeed seepage was a danger that

F

persisted long after nineteenth-century water companies had laid down iron pipes, rapidly changing pressure causing leaks at pipe junctions and, in reverse, the sucking in of infected material from the subsoil. Little wonder that until relatively recent years such scourges as typhoid and diarrhoea, to say nothing of cholera, were not infrequent.

Nevertheless, the first half of the nineteenth century did see in Hertfordshire a slow awakening to the desirability of a more abundant, and at the same time purer, water supply—an awakening no doubt encouraged by the cheaper manufacture of iron piping that had followed the immense expansion of the iron industry during the previous half-century. In 1833 Joseph Fowler established a waterworks at St Albans (which first had gas lighting seven years earlier) and was given permission to lay pipes in the public roads. About 1840 Hertford, some fifteen years after it had become gas lit, opened a waterworks on Port Hill. It took an outbreak of cholera in 1854 to persuade Watford to open a waterworks about twenty years after it had adopted gas. Hitchin built a reservoir with pumping engine attached on Windmill Hill in 1852, Berkhamsted opened a waterworks in 1864 and Hemel Hempstead in 1866. In 1873 the Colne Valley Water Co was formed, at first serving Aldenham, Elstree and Bushey but later extending its mains over a wider area. Ware followed suit in about 1880 and Hoddesdon in 1886. Two years later came the Rickmansworth and Uxbridge Valley Water Co. But the majority of villages remained outside the scope of these developments—a typical example was South Mimms, where the Medical Officer of the Board of Health reported in 1887 that its water was drawn from a polluted pond and a deep well fitted with a tackle so heavy as to be almost impossible to work. Not that well water was without its partisans; as late as 1900, when piped water was planned to replace a well declared impure, a crowded protest meeting at Redbourn declared that 'we are using water from the same source as has been used for years and years. There are people living here now ninety years old, who have always used it.'

By the early part of the twentieth century virtually all Hertford-shire public supplies were in the hands of small limited liability companies; some were later taken over by local authorities. In the 1950s the Ministry of Housing and Local Government urged amal-gamation into larger units, either by private Act or by ministerial directive. Today therefore Hertfordshire is covered by three statu-tory companies—the Lea Valley Water Company, the Colne Valley Water Co and the Rickmansworth and Uxbridge Valley Water Co. Watford Corporation, however, still retains its water department serving the borough.

In a dozen villages are relics which, though not in themselves of great age, may in some cases at least carry the mind back to more primitive times. Obviously no early settlement could establish itself without a reasonably secure water supply; how far can it be assumed that the position of surviving parish pumps gives a clue to the original place of settlement? It is certainly significant that those at Ardeley, Braughing, Cottered, Newnham and Offley are all near the church; at Buntingford, though the original settlement was on the now un-inhabited hilltop of Layston half a mile off, the pump near the cross-roads at the bottom of the village may just possibly suggest the posi-tion of the first permanent break-away from Layston. At Sarratt the first settlement clustered round the church, now (except for the manor house and rectory) almost deserted; Sarratt Green, with its pump in the middle (plate, page 107), appears to have become fringed with houses in the seventeenth century. In the middle of the village green too, are the pumps at Preston and Westmill; at Herting-fordbury five primitive wellheads are suggestively placed on the five small outlying greens of the parish—Birch Green, Cole Green, East End Green, Letty Green and Staines Green. At Anstey, Cottered, Hexton and Watton the pumps are at road junctions.

It would be unwise, however, to assume much on this score. None of the datable gears is earlier than the nineteenth century, most of them late in the century at that; the rest can safely be judged to fall within the same bracket, though at Offley the present pump (by

C. J. Ells, Luton), replacing an earlier and simpler one, was not installed until about 1920. Those at Braughing, Buntingford, Hexton, Newnham, Watton and Westmill are of the simple handle type, the others are worked by wheel and plunger, at Anstey made by Tasker and Co (now Taskers of Andover Ltd) about 1892, at Cottered by R. J. & J. Wilder, Wallingford, Berks, and at Newnham by C. P. Martin, Harpenden. The wellheads at Hertingfordbury are merely containing walls of brick surmounted by a semi-circular iron arch with iron pulley wheel. No village pump anywhere in the county is still in use.

Wellhead gears attached to dwelling houses are certainly more numerous than the handful revealed by haphazard research. Those so far recorded are nearly all of the same elementary type—iron wheel about 4 ft in diameter, with wooden spindle some 4 ft wide directly above the well; though most of the cottages near to which the gears stand are of the eighteenth century, it would be risky to date the gears themselves so early. From a certain elegance of design it is, however, tempting to suggest an early date for the wholly wooden gear (wheel 5 ft 6 in diameter, spindle 2 ft 6 in wide) in the main building—eighteenth century or earlier—of Dane End Farm, Redbourn. At Bonners Farm, Flamstead, is a gear alongside a well still used for drinking purposes and also scheduled as a static source by the Hertfordshire Fire Service; in a weatherboarded and tiled shed open on one side, it consists of an oak wheel 7 ft in diameter, 3 in wide, with iron turning handle, and an oak gear wheel with hornbeam cogs attached to a spindle 4 ft wide, the rope of which draws a bucket over a wheel of 18 in diameter, fixed above the wellhead and high in the oak frame that contains the whole gear. Bonners Farm belongs to the seventeenth century. In a different category altogether is a gear in the front garden of a house at Wheathampstead—an iron wheel with turning handle operating a single cylinder in the well top and discharging water through a standpipe outside the low brick wall surrounding the wellhead. It was made at an unknown date by Hayward Tyler Ltd, then of London, now of Luton.

Messrs Hayward Tyler are also the makers of two treble-acting pumps coupled by wood-toothed gearing to a wooden waterwheel at Hunton Bridge, north of Watford. They were used to pump water from the river Gade to the mansion of Langleybury, situated on an adjacent hillside, and may possibly date from 1856, when Langley-bury was enlarged and modernised. Later work on them, its exact nature unknown, was carried out by Roberts, millwright, of Bushey, now A. T. Roberts Ltd. The wooden wheel itself, no longer quite complete, may date from 1795 or the years immediately following, when an Act for certain improvements in the Grand Junction Canal, then under construction, provided for the removal and rebuilding 'in the most convenient and beneficial Situation' of 'the Engine which supplies a House called Langley Bury with water'. The whole appliance is said to have continued in use until about 1939.

In the Rickmansworth area—at Croxley House and Chorley Wood House—are two unusual gears, the former probably dating from 1770, when the house was built, the latter from about 1880 and still in use. The Croxley gear, which stands over a 250 ft well, consists of a series of large and small wooden cogwheels mounted in a wooden frame and operated by hand; these set in motion a toothed wheel over which the lifting chain passes. At Chorley Wood House (now owned by Chorley Wood Urban District Council) the gear is contained in a small brick building over the river Chess, which drives the main wheel, of cast iron 10 ft in diameter, 2 ft wide, with 30 paddle blades. It turns 1 rpm, driving a 3-cylinder pump over the well below.

But Hertfordshire's two most interesting gears—very different from each other in type—are found, one at Annables Farm, Kins-bourne Green, Harpenden, the other in Ashridge College of Management, Berkhamsted.

The Annables one is a large, vertical, oak donkey wheel 13 ft 6 in in diameter, 3 ft 4 in wide, with lateral struts for the walking donkey; it draws water from a well 146 ft deep (plate, page 90). Practically all its timbers appear to be the originals, a few now held together by iron plates. The present building of Annables Farm is of no great age; but close at hand is Annables Manor, which, though considerably rebuilt, can show Tudor fragments; it is said that the wheel, last worked in about 1901, itself dates from the seventeenth century. It stands in a narrow wooden shed with tiled roof; alongside is an equally narrow stable for the donkey; and just under the roof—so small that one wonders how he could have squeezed himself into it—is the space in which the donkey man slept. Though now unworked, the whole apparatus is in good workable condition and appears to be well cared for.

It was the Duke of Bridgewater who in his last years planned the rebuilding of the Egerton ancestral mansion of Ashridge, which had once been a medieval monastery, though the work was carried out by his successor in the years following 1808. In the course of it he replaced an old wooden horizontal horse wheel (mentioned as far back as 1575) above the medieval well 280 ft deep by a far more elaborate structure in cast iron. A detailed description of this was given to the present writer by Mr Rex Wailes, FSA, MIMechE:

> The shaft is inclined at 10–15 degrees; the whole structure is of cast iron moulded on a framework of iron on top of the well. A wooden plinth surrounds the framework, which latter is of spider construction with cast-iron built-up hub and 8 X-section arms. The shaft is 4 in diameter and carries a down-turned cast-iron bevel wheel with 8 T-arms and intermediate wrought-iron bases from shaft to rim. Across the top of the wellhead, connecting the frame, is an H sub-frame consisting of 2 T-section cast-iron braces extending right across from side to side and connected at the centre by a flat plate cast integral, which carries the thrust bearing the shaft. A bevel wheel has 84 teeth, 3-in pitch, and drives a cast-iron pinion with 24 teeth mounted on a 3-throw iron crank shaft. This drives a 3-cyclinder pump, which is mounted far below the top of the well. At the top of the driving shaft is an 18 ft cast-iron beam, at each end of which is a U-shaped yoke 2 ft wide, with 2 hooks for traces on each side. Height to beam varies from 6 ft maximum to 4 ft 6 in minimum.

A horizontal horse-wheel, rather similar to that at Ashridge but simpler in construction and now abandoned, can be seen under a tiled canopy in the park of Gorhambury, St Albans; it probably dates from twenty or thirty years after the erection of the mansion in

1777. A building near the ruins of the earlier Gorhambury, home of Sir Francis Bacon, suggests by its shape that it too may have contained a horizontal wheel, of which no trace now remains.

Between about 1808 and about 1860 the Ashridge gear was in regular use; its relinquishment followed the building in 1856 by Lord Brownlow, the then owner of Ashridge, of a waterworks in the adjacent village of Little Gaddesden, with a main to Ashridge itself. Part of this waterworks, looking very much like a mid-Victorian school house, stands over a well 275 ft deep, with its original boilers 20 ft long and 6 ft 6 in in diameter by Easton & Amos, London, still in occasional use. The Ashridge Water Co was absorbed by the Berkhamsted Water Co in 1948, which became part of the Rickmansworth and Uxbridge Valley Water Co three years later.

Technical developments and the pressure of rapidly expanding service demands have inevitably removed almost all traces of the old water companies—at their Bushey station, for instance, the Colne Valley Water Co had two beam engines, bought secondhand in 1873, and an 1890 diesel pump by Mirless Bickerton and Day, Stockport, all working satisfactorily when ordered to be sold for scrap in about 1955. At St Albans there are two cast-iron tanks dating from 1873 and 1888 respectively. Three pumping stations at Hertford, one built in 1840, one in 1862 and largely rebuilt in 1900, the third a former watermill rebuilt in 1880, are still in use by the Lea Valley Water Co. Watford Corporation Water Department preserves its original 1854 buildings in Local Board Lane, now using them as a store.

THE NEW RIVER

Whether the New River belongs to Hertfordshire or to London is a moot point; but since its head springs and about a third of its course are in the former, it may legitimately be included here.

Constructed between 1608 and 1613, the New River, some 15–20 ft wide but of no great depth, was designed to augment London's water supply by the flow from the then abundant Chadwell Spring, between Hertford and Ware, and from a large spring at Great Amwell about a mile away. The City Corporation having proved dilatory in spite of an outbreak of plague in 1603, Hugh (later Sir Hugh) Myddleton, Alderman of London, MP for Denbigh and with mining interests in Cardiganshire, undertook the immense work at his own cost; but with only a quarter accomplished he was forced to seek financial assistance. The corporation declining to lift a finger in a project that was, after all, to its own enormous advantage, James I at last came to the rescue, covering himself by accepting the promise of half the eventual profits of the enterprise. Against difficulties of all kinds Myddleton pressed on; and when the entire 40 miles of waterway (now somewhat shortened) had been completed, a grand assemblage (which, since the court was present, the corporation was not ashamed to attend) heralded the first water from Chadwell to flow into the reservoir known as the New River Head at Clerkenwell, whence it was to be conveyed in wooden pipes to various points of the city.

In 1619 the New River Company was formed by Myddleton, with 36 Adventurers' shares and another 36 reserved to the King. But no dividend was declared until 1633, two years after Myddleton's death, and then only an insignificant one; whereupon Charles I returned the Royal Moiety, as it was called, accepting in its place a fee-farm rent of £500 a year. The Royal Moiety was divided as King's shares among the holders of Adventurers' shares; and from then onwards the value of all New River shares began to rise, then to soar, maintaining an extraordinarily high level for two centuries. In 1727 a King's share changed hands for 5,000 guineas; in 1813 an Adventurers' share fetched £8,000 and in 1838 a full £18,000. Cussans in his *History of Hertfordshire* (Hertford Hundred) (1876) records that 'at a sale held in May 1873, four-sixteenths of a King's share were sold by the trustees of the late William Astell Esq at an average price of £3,060 each. During the previous year each sixteenth was entitled to a dividend of £112. 3s. 2d.' Apart from human nature's love of a gamble, the maintenance of such extraordinary values over so long a period may be attributed, among other things, to the manner in which the company coped with the gigantic problems arising from the growth of London (though there were plenty of contemporary grumbles), to the increasing value of the company's buildings and equipment and to the steady rise in land values along the whole course of the waterway. The company continued operating until 1904, when the New River was taken over by the Metropolitan Water Board, formed in the previous year. It then continued as a landholding company only, having no concern with water supply, and paying a dividend of $13\frac{1}{2}$ per cent in 1969.

Part of the old company's success was certainly due to two of its chief engineers, father and son—Robert Mylne (1733–1811) and William Chadwell Mylne (1781–1862), both of whom are buried in the churchyard of Great Amwell, overlooking the spring from which the New River drew part of its supply. Robert is probably best known as the designer of the first Blackfriars Bridge over the Thames, a column from which now stands in the garden of the house at Great Amwell in which William spent his old age; Robert's service, and William's, to the New River Company together cover a century pregnant with change. William was, indeed, responsible for (did he even devise?) the outstanding item of equipment in its possession.

By the early eighteenth century the growth of London was already demanding a much greater water supply; and at the same time Chadwell Spring showed signs of flagging. In 1738 therefore the company promoted a Bill enabling them to draw a measured quantity of water from the river Lea by means of a balance engine or gauge. A cut was made from the Lea to the New River and over it the gauge was erected. This was replaced in 1770 by a larger gauge designed by Robert Mylne and enclosed in a massive marble chest like a sarcophagus, now empty. Then in 1856 William Chadwell Mylne built the New Gauge, still in use, alongside the Lea itself. It is said to be unique (plate, page 107).

Housed in a substantial yellow-brick, slate-roofed building which also contains the dwelling house of the keeper, the gauge comprises two iron boats about 15 ft in length floating at Lea level, which are joined by a semi-elliptical iron beam some 28 ft long. This beam is connected vertically with a sluice gate between Lea and cut. The boats rise and fall with the rise and fall of the Lea, thus in part controlling the fall of water over the sluice, which can be further controlled by the adjustment of weights suspended from the gate. The daily inflow from the Lea averages 22½ million gallons.

Mylne the younger, who, like his father, was an architect as well as an engineer, was also responsible for the earliest extant pumping station in Hertfordshire, that at Amwell Hill, in 1847; a no doubt unconscious tribute to him is the basic similarity of architectural style observable in all later New River pumping stations, even when built many years after his death. Amwell Hill was, of course, powered at first by steam (the near-by pumping station at Amwell Marsh, though not built until 1883 and now largely demolished, is said to have once housed a beam engine) but in the present century steam has virtually everywhere given way to electric drive—at Rye Common in 1935, Amwell Hill in 1944, Hoddesdon and Broxbourne in 1946 and Turnford, Cheshunt, in 1953. Broadmead, close to Chadwell Spring, was operated by steam until 1967 but is soon to be converted to electricity; it contains a 50 hp vertical single cylinder marine engine, with fly wheel of 11 ft 2 in diameter, by J. Simpson & Co, London, installed in 1900. At Turnford, now disconnected and admirably preserved, is a 90 hp single cylinder, double acting, inverted jet condensing side lever paddle type marine engine by Boulton & Watt, originally operated by the Hampstead Water Co in 1847. When that company was taken over by the New River Company in 1856 the engine was transferred to Turnford, where it remained in use for many years.

The meanderings of the New River and later road developments have combined to bring into existence in Hertfordshire nineteen road-river bridges and a few others in which the river is crossed by a footpath. Of the road-river bridges, ten have been rebuilt in quite recent years; the earliest of the remaining nine carries a small side road from Amwell End to Great Amwell and consists of two iron girders resting on brick piers concreted over and having a span of about 18 ft, with cross girders producing a width of about 12 ft; its height above the river is only about 3 ft. One girder is stamped 'New River Co 1824 Priestfields Iron Works near Bilston'. The plain handrail is modern.

Other dated bridges are found at Flamstead End, Cheshunt (1835), Mill Lane, Broxbourne (1841), Wormley Hill (1841), the Lynch, Hoddesdon (1842) and Station Road, Broxbourne (1868). The latticed side rails at Wormley Hill and Hoddesdon are stamped 'Hunter London' and at Broxbourne a girder has 'Cochrane Grove & Co'. Bridges at Great Amwell, Stanstead St Margaret's, and two at Spital-brook, Hoddesdon, bear neither date nor ironfounder's name but their style, though varying somewhat from bridge to bridge, puts them fairly plainly into the mid-nineteenth century.

CHAPTER FIVE

Roads, Waterways, Railways and Posting Boxes

FOR a century, and particularly during the second half of it, Hertfordshire has received and absorbed an increasing share of the gigantic out-thrust of London. In 1861, with a population of 173,000, fully one-third of its people had been born in the county and its few industries were those that might have been found there a century before that. In 1961 its population had risen to 832,000, of whom an enormous majority were what old Hertfordshire folk would have called 'foreigners'; a host of new industries had been drawn principally from London but also from elsewhere and its traditional industries—except papermaking and printing—had become sadly diminished both in scope and in importance. In this transformation, developing communications played a vital part.

ROADS

Three great Roman roads radiate from London through Hertfordshire—the road to York, later called Ermine Street, later still the Old North Road and now A10; Watling Street, now A5, through Verulamium (St Albans) to Chester; and a third leaving Verulamium for Cirencester but joined at Nash Mills, near Hemel Hempstead, by a road from London through Bushey and Watford, the whole being later known as Akeman Street, now A411 to Hunton Bridge near Watford, and A41 thereafter. A fourth radial—the Great North Road (A1000, A1 and B197)—dates as a thoroughfare to the north only from the seventeenth century, though parts of its Hertfordshire stretch are Roman. Local Roman roads still survive in a few modern crossroads or country lanes.

Basically, therefore, the Roman road system is also that of today—apart, of course, from such modern motorways as M1 or A1 (M). This is not the place to discuss the entire history of roads, but to comment on them only in relation to industry. In post-Roman days, through the Middle Ages and down to at least the end of the seventeenth century, they suffered progressive deterioration—the records of travellers, describing potholes in which one could drown, or highwaymen appearing out of a dense cloud of dust, can be left to tell their own tale. It was not until the rise of the turnpike system that something like consistent improvement began.

As was shown in Chapter Two, it may be said that the malting industry of Ware was in a sense responsible for the creation of that system. By the mid-seventeenth century, when travelling was steadily becoming more common, Ermine Street south of Huntingdonshire, neglected for centuries, had become so decayed as to be virtually unusable by reason of the heavily laden wagons and long trains of pack-horses bringing barley to Ware maltsters from all over the eastern counties. So loud grew the outcry that in 1663 Parliament broke through the ancient policy of leaving road maintenance to parish supervision by passing an Act putting a long section of Ermine Street into the hands of the justices of Hertfordshire, Cambridgeshire and Huntingdonshire, with power to defray the cost of maintenance by tolls on road users. Three turnpike gates were authorised; actually the only one to function was at Wadesmill. The road continued under the jurisdiction of the justices until 1733, when its Hertfordshire section, from Wadesmill to Royston, was taken over by a Wadesmill Turnpike Trust composed at first of local gentry, parsons and influential farmers. South of Wadesmill the Cheshunt Turnpike Trust had been created in 1725.

Productive though the turnpike trusts were in many ways, they suffered from the same disadvantage as had the parishes before them, in that their control was restricted to one arbitrarily delimited length of what we should now call a trunk road; the care of the road as a continuous whole was not provided for. A typical instance of this is

Turnpike roads

1 Sparrows Herne
2 Dunstable - St Albans - London
3 Luton - St. Albans
4 St. Albans - South Mimms
5 Hatfield-Reading
6 Whetstone (Middlesex)
7 Galley Corner
8 Welwyn
9 Stevenage - Biggleswade
10 Hitchin
11 Watton
12 Icknield
13 Wadesmill
14 Cheshunt
15 Hockerill

Bishop's
Stortford

Ware

Hertford

Hatfield

Baldock

Hitchin

Barnet

St. Albans

Watford

Tring

N

0 2 4 6 8
Miles

seen in the turnpiking of the Great North Road. A trust was established along it from Highgate, Middlesex, to Barnet in 1712, and extended to an inn (the predecessor of the present-day Duke of York) south of Potters Bar in 1720. In that year a trust was created to control the section north of Stevenage through Baldock to Biggleswade in Bedfordshire. Then in 1726 the road from Lemsford Mill, Hatfield, to Stevenage came under the control of another trust, and—at last—in 1730 the section from the Duke of York to Lemsford Mill was turnpiked. Not until 1730, therefore, could a traveller along the Great North Road through Hertfordshire begin to expect to find a road which might be kept in something like reasonable repair throughout the whole length of the county.

Other roads, all of them sections of longer thoroughfares, were turnpiked as time went on: the old road from Barnet to St Albans through Kit's End and Dancers Hill (part unclassified, part A6) in 1715; from Dunstable, Beds, through St Albans towards London (A5) in 1722; from Luton, Beds, to St Albans (A6) in 1727. Later changes were: from Harlow, Essex, through Sawbridgeworth and Bishop's Stortford to Cambridge (A11) in 1744; from Hertford to Broadwater, south of Stevenage (A602) in 1757; from Hitchin to Bedford (A600) in 1757; from Hatfield to Reading, Berks, through St Albans, Watford and Rickmansworth (A414, A405, A412 and A404) also in 1757; from Bushey through Watford and Tring to Aylesbury, Bucks (A411 and A41) in 1762; from Dunstable through Luton, Hitchin, Baldock and Royston to Cambridge (A505) in 1769. This last route followed fairly closely the Iron Age track known as the Icknield Way. In 1804 Arthur Young in his *General View of the Agriculture of Hertfordshire* could write that 'the roads of a county so near to the Metropolis can scarcely be bad; six great leading turnpikes passing through so small a district would alone give it this character, but there are many cross-roads nearly as good as turnpikes'. Which is not, of course, to deny that there were also bad roads (some very bad) in the county. But to study the records of any turnpike trust over more than a century is to watch the constant re-routing, straightening, widening and surfacing undertaken by trust surveyors—on the whole an admirable body of men, most of them part-time employees and all only amateurs. Not until the days of McAdam and Telford did the specialist road engineer come into his own.

It was McAdam (living at Hoddesdon between 1825 and 1836) who was particularly associated with Hertfordshire as surveyor to, ultimately, many of the trusts in the county. In the second decade of the nineteenth century Telford remodelled the Holyhead Road (dealing with several dozen trusts on the way) through Barnet, St Albans and Dunstable and in the 1820s made elaborate surveys for a similar, though finally abortive, remodelling of the Great North Road. Inns along all turnpike roads throve as never before; though many have since vanished, Baldock still has its George and Dragon, Berkhamsted its King's Arms, Bishop's Stortford its George, Hitchin its Sun, Redbourn its Bull, Puckeridge its Crown and Falcon, St Albans its Peahen, Red Lion and White Hart, Welwyn its White Hart, and there are others of lesser note. As both vehicle design and the breeding of horses improved, the speed and convenience of coach travel were greatly increased; and even allowing for occasional moments of novelists' licence to writers like Dickens, it is demonstrable that the early nineteenth century saw such feats of transportation as had never been possible before, almost entirely owing to the conscientious labours of turnpike trusts. A large pinch of salt is necessary, however, when reading the romantic exaggerations concerning 'coaching days' produced later by nostalgic conservatives of the Railway Age.

An aspect of early communications that has persisted almost into modern times deserves closer investigation by industrial archaeologists than it appears to have received. To what extent did the old carriers' carts, carrying both passengers and goods, transport industrial materials? All large industrial concerns maintained their own fleets of wagons; but who served lesser industrialists for this purpose? The big firm of Pickford (now absorbed into British Road Services) developed in part out of a local carrier's business at Markyate Street,

Page 107 (above) *Village pump at Sarratt;* (below) *New River intake gauge of 1856, Hertford*

Page 108 (above) *Inscribed milestone on B1001 between Watton and Ware;* (below) *milestone at Hamels Park, Puckeridge*

in north-west Hertfordshire, to become a nationally known haulage contractor.

Few turnpike trusts prospered financially; some had a constant struggle to keep solvent. With even the suggestion of a railway in their locality their revenue invariably dropped; when the railway in fact arrived the trust virtually collapsed. In Hertfordshire after 1862 trusts began to dissolve and turnpiked roads to be taken over by local highway boards. After 1878 half the cost of the upkeep of disturnpiked roads was paid out of county funds and ten years later control of all main roads was vested in the newly formed county councils. Though trunk roads are now the concern of the Ministry of Transport, the present-day policy of the Hertfordshire County Council is understood to envisage improvement to only a limited number of cross-country traffic routes, leaving many country lanes (which in this county are very charming) in little more than decent repair.

Such turnpike relics as tollhouses are rare in Hertfordshire—only one, half-timbered, with brick infilling (very different from the conventional design) and built about 1728, has been definitely identified, though others may still await discovery. It stands on the Great North Road opposite Ayot Green, just south of Welwyn; on the dissolution of the Welwyn Trust it and another (now demolished) were sold together for £24 10s.

Milestones, on the other hand are relatively common; 78 still in position are listed in Appendix Two of the Gazetteer, though road operations tend to reduce their number. About 60 are stone, the rest cast iron. In 1742 the Wadesmill Trust, and in 1743 the Cheshunt Trust, set up milestones along their roads—that is, the whole Hertfordshire stretch of the modern A10—and most stone milestones can fairly confidently be attributed to the eighteenth century. But in 1804 the Cheshunt Trust resolved to cover the original incised mileage inscription with 'the iron plate produced by Mr McAdam'[1] and most other trusts appear to have followed suit, though a few preferred to

---

[1] This appears to be an early recognition of McAdam's interest in roads. It was only some years later that he began to experiment in actual road construction.

G

recut the original inscriptions. By the 1820s iron milestones became the fashion, at any rate as replacements; the earliest of these, made in about 1822 by Wilder & Sons (now John Wilder Ltd) of Reading, can be seen on the Hatfield–Reading Turnpike between Hatfield and St Albans; two, made by R. J. & J. Barratt, London, and dated 1826, are at Tring and two more, by Brown & Green of Luton (established 1840), are alongside the Luton–St Albans road, A6. Others bear no maker's name or date.

Only two dated stone milestones have so far been found. The first is at Bell Bar, North Mymms, discovered in 1965 as threshold of a front door and obviously transferred at some unknown date from Stanborough—it stands opposite the seventeenth stone in the regular series. On its battered face can be read 'XXI Mil. . . . ndon'; almost untraceable but more clearly seen in photographs is a date, 1745. The second stone stands in the middle of a hedge nearly midway on the road from Watton to Ware, B1001. On its rear side, so sharply incised that it might have been cut yesterday, is the legend (probably referring to the road, not the stone), 'Repaird by a Voluntary Subscription from the Inhabitants of Ware 1751.' This road was not turnpiked until 1757 (plate, page 108). Unfortunately the Hertfordshire County Record Office has neither the early records of the Watton Trust nor the Ware surveyors' accounts for that year, leaving both the repair and the reason for so permament a commemoration a mystery.

These stones are not, however, the earliest in Hertfordshire; two at Barkway and two at Barley can be dated from documentary evidence at between 1728 and 1732. In 1586 Dr William Mowse, Master of Trinity Hall, Cambridge, left in his will £1,000 to mend the highways *in et circa nostram villam et praecipue versus Barkway*. To this sum his executor, Robert Hare, added £600. To what extent, if any, the benefaction was at once applied is not known; in the early eighteenth century Dr William Warren, a later Master, acting under the will, set up the existing milestones along the whole length of road between the two places. The four stones in Hertfordshire now carry nineteenth-century iron plates, the final stone at Barkway also bearing the arms of Trinity Hall and of Hare—only Mowse, the original benefactor, is forgotten. It may be noted that the road from Puckeridge through Barkway to the county boundary at Barley was included in the Wadesmill Trust in 1733; the road from the county boundary to Cambridge was turnpiked in 1724.

What may conceivably be an even earlier stone stands a quarter of a mile up the drive of Hamels Park, Puckeridge, once again on the Wadesmill Trust road. In appearance it resembles a gravestone, unlike any others on the road (placed in 1742) or, indeed, in the county; on one side (fairly recently recut) is 'XXVIII Miles from Shore Ditch Church London' and on the other '& XXIII Miles ¾ from Cambridge', (plate, page 108). In 1745 the trust minute book notes that the northern road (that is, the road to Royston) at the twenty-eighth milestone is to be widened and that William Freeman Esq has given land for that purpose. Freeman lived at Hamels; since the present twenty-eighth milestone conforms in type to all others along the road, did he claim the old one, possibly a late seventeenth-century relic, as souvenir of the transaction?

Finally a brief note may be made of two stone milestones unconnected with turnpikes. They stand on an unclassified road from Little Gaddesden through Nettleden to Hemel Hempstead and appear to have been set up in the first years of the nineteenth century by the seventh Earl of Bridgewater, successor of the Canal Duke and builder of the present mansion of Ashridge, to which the road forms a distant approach.

In the days before service stations dispensed drink to mechanical vehicles the problem of watering horses was conveniently (and no doubt profitably) solved by roadside innkeepers, who placed a wooden, hand-filled water trough, or perhaps two water troughs, outside their premises. In the 1870s the Metropolitan Drinking Fountain and Cattle Trough Association began to establish, in Hertfordshire as elsewhere, large granite troughs linked to a permanent water supply, usually with a small ground-level trough for dogs and a push-button fountain for human beings. Only five of them are still to be found in the county—at Bushey, Hatfield, Potters Bar, Croxley Green and Rickmansworth—sometimes empty, occasionally filled with flowers, more often with litter. Nobody appears to set any value upon them; as relics of a transport age now utterly vanished are they not as worthy of attention and preservation as many more acknowledged ones?

Of the several hundred road bridges in the county none is of outstanding quality, though a few deserve brief mention here and others that can be definitely dated are included in the Gazetteer. At the same time, very many small red-brick bridges, sometimes steeply humped and overhung by the hedges or trees of country lanes, fit so delightfully into their rural surroundings that they can easily be missed by the casual explorer and are completely at the mercy of the road improver, who scarcely stops to think that he is destroying good country craftsmanship of the eighteenth or early nineteenth century. Such bridges were usually built and maintained by the parish vestry; where a river or other obstacle on a main thoroughfare had been bridged before the creation of a turnpike trust the bridge was in the hands of the county justices, though its later maintenance might be shared between them and the trust. Bridges built by a trust—for example, over a former ford—were trust-owned but were handed over to the county when the trust was dissolved.

Hertford's oldest bridge appears to be St Michael's bridge, St Albans, carrying the pre-1830 line of Watling Street over the river Ver; built in 1765, it is of red brick with stone coping, 32 ft in width, and has three low semi-circular arches of 5 ft, 8 ft and 5 ft span. Such smaller bridges as, for instance, at Lemsford, carrying the pre-1833 line of the Great North Road and having a width of only 24 ft, may be taken as typical of a great number built in the eighteenth and early nineteenth centuries by various trusts. Near Tonwell, on B1001, is a red-brick, two-arched bridge with brick wing walls and stone cutwater on one side bearing the date 1792.

Two road bridges that, on their modest scale, may rank among Hertfordshire's best are at Wadesmill, north of Ware (plate, page 125), and at London Colney. That at Wadesmill, carrying the A10 over the river Rib, is of grey brick, 31 ft wide and with two semi-circular arches of 25 ft span resting centrally on seven round stone pillars which, by allowing light to penetrate the underside of the arches, give the whole structure an agreeably buoyant aspect. Until 1966, when a large section was destroyed by a lorry, it retained its original latticed iron side rails. It was built in 1825 by Brough & Smith, London, on the order of the Cheshunt Trust, although, as a county bridge, its cost was shared by the justices.

The London Colney bridge carries A6 over the river Colne; it is extremely graceful in outline, apparently the work of a local designer and builder in 1772. It was mentioned as wanting repair in 1828. With embanked approaches, it follows a gentle unbroken curve above its seven semi-circular arches of 5 ft, 8 ft, 11 ft, 13 ft, 11 ft, 8 ft and 5 ft span. The three middle arches are built over inverted arches in the bed of the river. Originally it had brick parapets, for which plain iron railings were substituted—probably for the better—when the footway was jettied out in 1948.

Two picturesque bridges over the river Gade near Great Gaddesden, about a quarter of a mile apart on the road from Hemel Hempstead to Dagnall, Bucks (B486), are favourite subjects for photographers. The Gade at this point is for the most part sedgy and backed by a steep tree-covered hillside with a foreground of lush meadow; the bridges themselves, of colour-washed brick, have a superficially medieval aspect, with three pointed arches of 20 ft span and stone-capped cutwaters. Actually they were built shortly after 1800, on a diversion of the road; but one is only 18 ft in width and the other is approached at each end by an almost right-angled turn. How long, one wonders, can they be expected, in spite of their undoubted charm, to survive the demands of modern traffic?

All the bridges described so far have been of brick or stone. At Waterford, on A602, are three, two of them small, the other rather larger, having brick abutments and wing walls but iron girder decks and rather handsomely designed iron side rails of 1869. Built in the previous year, and very typical of its period, is a bridge over four tracks of the old Midland Railway main line at Radlett. With brick abutments and wing walls, it is decked with iron girders, the spandrels of the arch bracings containing a quatrefoil design; but its former arcaded side rails were, when last seen, covered by unsightly corrugated iron sheeting.

The most attractive iron footbridge in the county, however, stands in Gadebridge Park, Hemel Hempstead, formerly the grounds of the mansion of the Paston Cooper family (plate, page 125). The work of a local craftsman, John Cranstone (see page 91) and built about 1840, it has stone abutments, an iron girder deck with segmented arch bracing and decorative spandrels, and elaborately decorated iron side rails splayed at each end of the bridge to two terminal pillars. Whether Cranstone designed it himself or adapted a published design is uncertain; but certainly his bridge alone would make Hemel Hempstead worth a visit.

Those who enjoy solving puzzles may profitably study a bridge, built in 1908, that spans first the mill stream of Broxbourne Mill, then two tracks of the old Great Eastern Railway's line to Cambridge, lastly the New River. It is approached on the east by a road from Nazeing, Essex, rising on 14 brick arches, at the top of which it is joined on the south by another rising, brick-arched road from Broxbourne Mill. Then, with a slight change of direction, it crosses mill stream and Lea by a bridge of about 30 ft span; after which it is joined on the north by yet another rising brick-arched road (now closed) from an unoccupied site. Next, reverting to its former direction, it crosses, first an empty space about 20 ft wide by a second through bridge, then two tracks of railway by a bridge of about 40 ft span alongside Broxbourne station. Lastly, just beyond the station, it crosses the New River by a bridge of slightly wider carriageway than the others, emerging on to high ground immediately afterwards. Throughout this dog-legged course the road is narrow, rising

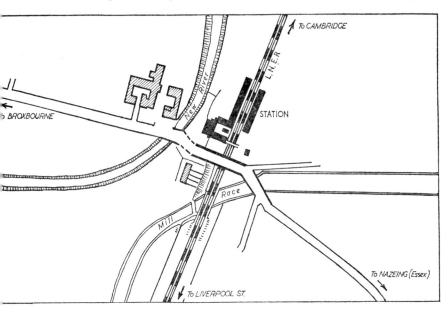

Plan of Broxbourne bridge

steadily over its whole length, and obscured by high brick parapets. It carries a road intended to replace the old way from Broxbourne to Nazeing, which incidentally involved payment of a toll at The Crown public house on the Essex side of the Lea. The northern road from the unoccupied site had apparently to be built, at considerable cost, to preserve a right of way from grazing ground beside the mill stream. But there is evidence to suggest that the frustrating dog-leg was not contemplated in the original design; what, then, can be the reason for it? And why, in a bridge so narrow and now become a fairly busy traffic route, do the parapets remain high enough to make it almost impossible to negotiate the dog-leg without extreme caution, especially since the side road from Broxbourne Mill joins the main carriage way at one end of it? A plan of this bridge is given above.

Two bridges over railways deserve attention. The first is at Knebworth, carrying a side road over four tracks of the old Great Northern Railway main line; it is of brick, with a single arch of 96 ft span and 48 ft height, built in 1850. The second is on the A10 between Puckeridge and Buntingford. It is a skew road-bridge superimposed on an iron girder bridge over the St Margaret's–Buntingford branch of the old Great Eastern Railway, opened in 1863.

WATERWAYS

Hertfordshire boasts no rivers of much size—the biggest of them, the Lea, could be matched in any county. The Lea's principal tributary, the Stort, is even smaller. Yet, as we have seen, in Chapter Two, to both these rivers Hertfordshire owes much of the prosperity of the malting industry in its heyday. On the west side of the county neither the Gade nor the Colne was navigable; it was left to the Grand Junction (now Grand Union) Canal at the turn of the eighteenth and nineteenth centuries very gradually to inject into that region the beginnings of a more than local industrial life.

The Lea, rising near Luton, Beds, flowing south-east and then south through Hertfordshire (which it leaves at Waltham Cross) and emptying itself into the Thames at Limehouse, was reputed to be navigable in some fashion as far as Ware and possibly Hertford in Saxon days. Thereafter, as century succeeded century, many Acts were passed with the intention of improving it, though chiefly with an eye to its London end; the long history of Ware is full of rivalries and quarrels between that town and Hertford over its local control. The upshot of both legislation and quarrelling was, however, equally ineffectual; not until the Lea Navigation Act of 1739 was the river brought for the first time under more or less unified direction over its entire navigable length. For the first time it was properly scoured, flashes removed and locks built at Ware, Stanstead and Broxbourne. In 1765 the trustees under the Act employed John Smeaton to make substantial new cuts, increase the number of locks and establish a continuous towpath; he was later followed by Thomas Telford.

Then, in 1868, the trustees gave way to the Lea Conservancy Board covering the whole catchment area. Abundant traffic demanded further improvements and these were constantly undertaken, among the last being the enlargement of the waterway during the First World War to take 100-ton vessels as far as Hertford and an entire reconstruction in 1922 of the locks between Hertford and Enfield, Middlesex. With nationalisation in 1948 the board gave way to the British Transport Commission, which in its turn handed over to the British Waterways Board in 1963.

To avoid possible misunderstanding it may be well to add that the Hertford Union Canal, completed in 1830, which joins the Lea Navigation to the Grand Union network by way of the Regent's Canal, lies wholly in London, not in Hertfordshire.

Before 1766 the Stort, which flows into the Lea at Fielde's Weir near Hoddesdon, had been little considered as a waterway, such craft as ventured on it from Bishop's Stortford having great difficulty in navigating it at all. In that year, however, the Stort Navigation Act, sponsored by Sir George Duckett of Bishop's Stortford and aided by an influential local innkeeper, Thomas Adderley, led to the dredging of the stream and the construction of adequate locks. But for various reasons the navigation never prospered, passing in the next century or so through a number of private hands and in 1905 into those of the Stort Navigation Company. The company enjoyed no greater success than previous owners; in 1911 it sold the whole navigation for the sum of 5s to the Lea Conservancy Board, which reconstructed it practically from end to end. But reconstruction came too late. The main defect of the navigation had always been that it terminated at Bishop's Stortford, leaving untapped the rich barley country to the north and north-east. At the end of the eighteenth century the Duke of Bridgewater had conceived a plan for continuing it into Norfolk and linking it with other canals in that region, employing John Rennie to make a survey; but after his death in 1803 the plan was allowed to lapse. And so for another century the vicious circle persisted—Bishop's Stortford trade dwindling because of a defective waterway and waterway improvements made unremunerative by declining trade. Several later attempts to include both Stort and Lea in a widespread East Anglian network also came to naught.

Today both navigations are little used except by pleasure craft, so that their character is unlikely to be altered by the Lea Valley Regional Park now in the course of construction. Indeed, all Hertfordshire waterways fall within the government's 1966 plan of waterway conservation largely for pleasure purposes.

From the cruising enthusiast's point of view, the 13 miles of the Stort, meandering quietly through green pastures only slightly disturbed by the new town at Harlow, Essex, is the more attractive. Between its junction with the Lea and Bishop's Stortford there are eight locks, most having lock houses; the pounds are long and tranquil. The Lea, on the other hand, has over its $11\frac{1}{4}$ miles in Hertfordshire ten locks with an average fall of 5 ft 10 in and a riverside scene of much more varied nature. Its most interesting point to the industrial archaeologist—the New Gauge between Ware and Hertford— has been described on page 99.

So much has been written on the Grand Junction (Union) Canal, notably by Charles Hadfield and L. T. C. Rolt, that only the briefest outline of its history is called for here.

Following a survey by James Barnes in 1792 and by William Jessop in the same year, an Act of 1793 authorised the building of a canal between the Thames at Brentford, Middlesex, and Braunston, Northants, on the edge of the large Midland complex centred on Birmingham, and using, in Hertfordshire, the valleys of the Colne, Gade and Bulbourne as its basic line. This Grand Junction Canal, as it was called, was completed as far as Hemel Hempstead in 1797 and Tring in 1799 and was opened as far as Stoke Bruerne, Northants, in 1800. From Tring ran an arm (in part a navigable feeder) to Wendover, Bucks; opened in 1799, it was closed to commercial traffic in 1896 and has since been largely filled up. From about 2 miles north of Tring ran the Aylesbury (Bucks) arm, surveyed by W. A. Provis in 1811 and opened in 1815, of which a length of $1\frac{3}{4}$ miles crosses

Hertfordshire at Long Marston and Puttenham. Between these two arms are now four large reservoirs in Hertfordshire and Buckinghamshire, built, some in, some before, 1838. An arm to Watford and St Albans was early mooted but never undertaken.

Providing as it did not only the shortest waterway route to London for an immense volume of traffic but also the only route open to craft built for such large rivers as the Thames and Trent, the canal prospered. The first threat to that prosperity came in 1838 from the London & Birmingham Railway, which hugged the canal along the greater part of its line and in Hertfordshire wove an intricate pattern with it along the whole length of the Gade and Bulbourne valleys. For three-quarters of a century the canal competed hard with the railway, though with slow yet inevitable loss. In 1894, by amalgamation with two other companies, it secured unified control to Leicester; in 1929, by amalgamation with three other companies, it secured virtually unified control to Birmingham, at the same time amalgamating with the Regent's Canal, London, and changing the name of the whole waterway system to the Grand Union Canal. In the next few years further control was obtained from Leicester to the Trent. Like the Lea and Stort Navigations, it was taken over in 1948 by the British Transport Commission and in 1963 by the British Waterways Board. In recent years commercial traffic has greatly diminished; but there is no doubt about its popularity with cruising enthusiasts.

Though all its best-known features and beauty spots lie outside the county, Hertfordshire can claim the highest point along its length of roughly 200 miles. At Coppermill Lock, Rickmansworth, where it leaves Middlesex, it is 127 ft 3 in above sea level. Thence to Cow Roast Lock, Wigginton (plate, page 126), it rises 255 ft 4 in, the steepest portion being north of Boxmoor, with eighteen locks in 7 miles and a rise of 119 ft. Beyond Wigginton it crosses the Chiltern escarpment in the Tring cutting, 382 ft 7 in above sea level, some $1\frac{1}{4}$ miles long and between 20 ft and 25 ft deep, then falling by a flight of seven locks with a total fall of 42 ft 3 in at Marsworth, Bucks. The depth of water in Hertfordshire varies from 5 ft 6 in to 8 ft.

There are in all 37 locks of 88 ft in length and 16 ft in width, each built to accommodate narrow boats in pairs, along its Hertfordshire stretch. Their masonry goes back basically to the first building of the canal, though it has, of course, been extensively repaired. Often the date of a replacement of their iron fittings (up to a century ago) is inscribed in the masonry; but oak lock gates must be renewed about every forty years. Present-day canal users operate the locks for themselves; but lock keepers' houses, the oldest dating from about 1810, some now occupied by maintenance staff, some empty, are still attached to 17 locks. Originally stone milestones along the towpath marked the distance southwards from Braunston; they were replaced in 1896 by metal plaques, all except two of which are still in position. A number of iron bollards, made at an unknown date by the London and Lancashire Engineering Company, are also to be seen.

When the canal was used principally by commercial traffic wharves were built at appropriate spots to facilitate the loading and unloading of barges and narrow boats. All except three have now vanished—Boxmoor Wharf, used by L. Rose Ltd at Hemel Hempstead and Apsley and Croxley wharves, used by John Dickinson Ltd in connection with their paper mills. At Dudswell, near Tring, there still stands an old warehouse, formerly part of the wharf there; but there is nothing left of the Albion wharf, Hemel Hempstead, attached to the Albion public house and at one time a coal wharf, or of the Rickmansworth wharf a quarter of a mile long, or of Lady Capel's wharf, north of Watford, where the duty on coal destined for the City of London was once collected.

Before the days of self-propelled craft, barges and narrow boats were drawn by horses, which were stabled for the night at such canal-side inns as the Fishery Inn, Hemel Hempstead, or the Three Horseshoes at Winkwell (near Bovingdon); the canal company does not appear to have provided stables of its own. Today, with no straining horses to cause deterioration, the towpath is in excellent condition and makes a very attractive waterside walk. Generally speaking, it keeps to the west bank, though sometimes—as at Cassiobury Park, Watford, for instance—it crosses to the east; this crossing dates from the first days of the canal, when the Earl of Essex, owner of Cassiobury Park and a member of the canal board, insisted upon running no risk of poachers on his estate. Elsewhere the crossings are less easy to account for; but of the 44 road bridges which span the canal in Hertfordshire 11 are crossover ones.

A list of these bridges, dated 1893, in the British Waterways Museum at Stoke Bruerne records the large majority as then being of brick with brick wing walls; their counterparts today are marked in the British Waterways Board's cruising booklet no 8. A few, such as Stockers, Rickmansworth, have even now not changed since the day they were built; but many have been either widened or partially or wholly reconstructed since the 1893 list was compiled. As a whole they offer a fairly comprehensive review of small bridge building in the nineteenth and twentieth centuries—building in brick, iron, steel or concrete. Rose Cottage bridge, Berkhamsted, having brick abutments, wing walls and parapet, is decked by iron girders bearing the date 1889, the year of its rebuilding. Not far away, Pix bridge, of much the same construction, has girders bearing the name of G. Deeley, Bilston, but no date. Very picturesque in its setting is a little one at Winkwell—a hand-operated swing bridge with timber deck 10 ft wide and a sign prohibiting loads of more than 2 tons. But the most popularly photographed bridge is at Grove Park, Watford (plate, page 126), carrying the approach road to the mansion of the Grove, formerly the seat of Lord Clarendon, now the Motor Drivers Training School of British Railways. It is early nineteenth century in date, of brick covered with stucco, having elegantly designed jack arches and a balustraded parapet. Not more than 15 ft wide, it is so steeply humped that in recent years it has been furnished with traffic lights; one wonders how Lord Clarendon, sitting stately in his carriage, managed to avoid an undignified abdominal heave when crossing it.

At Rickmansworth, where the river Chess, and also a short arm leading out of it to the gas works, now closed, enter the canal, there are two locks side by side, one in the canal (lock 81), the other in the river. A couple of hundred yards up the river, near its junction with a minor stream, is a modern lifting bridge over the latter, a replacement of an older but similar one, having a single leaf operated by pulleys in a cast-iron frame.

Finally two small bridges, also steeply humped, may be mentioned for their picturesqueness. They span the Aylesbury arm of the canal at Dixon's Gap, near Tring, and at Wilstone. Each is 10 ft wide, carries a country lane and plainly remains untouched since the opening of the arm in 1815.

RAILWAYS

In the field of industrial archaeology there is little of outstanding interest in Hertfordshire railways. The county contains no large industrial centres to justify important installations, no pronounced physical features to give rise to more than one or two engineering works of note. A certain old-fashioned charm, faintly surprising so near to London, and an awareness of social convenience that lingered until a few years ago, have since been expunged by brutal economic facts and subsequent instances of ruthlessness by British Railways without much apparent compensating advantage. In some respects the commuter is little better off than he was before these changes and what small railway individuality Hertfordshire formerly enjoyed has been lost.

Hertfordshire's railway pattern in its most expansive period closely followed its road pattern: four principal main lines and one smaller one radiating from London to East Anglia, the north and the northwest; and ten east-west lines, several of them promoted in the first instance by small private companies and not sited with overall county strategical wisdom. Indeed, in the words of a school geography book by R. Lydekker, published in 1909, 'it is frequently found convenient to hold important Hertfordshire meetings, like those of the County Council, in London'.

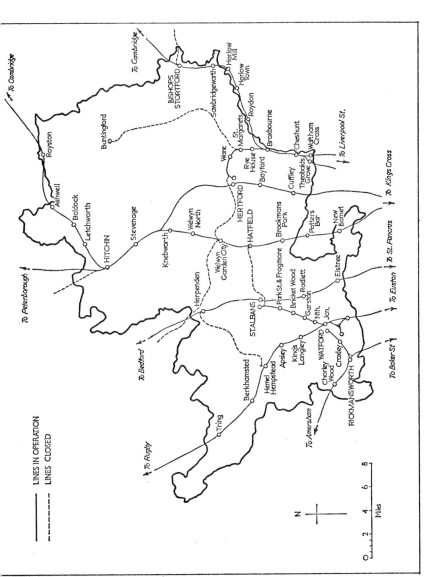

Railways

The first line to pass through Hertfordshire, by way of Watford and Berkhamsted, was the London & Birmingham Railway (after 1846 the London and North Western), which opened as far as Boxmoor in 1837 and through Tring to Birmingham in the following year. Next, in 1840, the Northern & Eastern Railway, which had projected a line to York, opened as far as Broxbourne, extending in 1841 to Harlow, Essex, and in 1842 to Bishop's Stortford and Cambridge. In 1862 the Northern & Eastern and the Eastern Counties Railway, to whom this line had been leased, became the Great Eastern Railway. Darlington was reached by the Great Northern Railway, which ran through Barnet, Hatfield and Hitchin, in 1850. But only in 1868 did the Midland Railway bring its line southward from Bedford to London, passing through Harpenden, St Albans and Elstree. Rather later, in 1887, the Metropolitan Railway pushed out to Rickmansworth and in 1889 by Chorleywood to Chesham, Bucks. Soon after the First World War electric trains came into operation between London and Watford and London and Barnet (Cockfosters).

Of the ten cross-country lines, most of them having only one track, only three are still open to passenger traffic, and the future of one of these seems uncertain. A branch of the Northern & Eastern Railway from Rye House, just north of Hoddesdon, to Ware and Hertford was opened in 1843; and in 1858 a branch of the London & North Western joined Watford to St Albans, which up to then had been isolated. Another St Albans branch line, opened in 1865 from Hatfield, was closed in 1951. A line from Hitchin to Royston, originally projected as part of an Oxford–Cambridge route, was opened in 1850 and extended to Cambridge in the following year. In 1857 a branch was opened from Hitchin through Bedford to the Midland Railway at Wigston, near Leicester; it was closed in 1962. Other lines which are now closed are: Hatfield to Hertford, opened in 1858, closed 1951; Hatfield to Wheathampstead and Luton, opened in 1860, closed 1965; St Margaret's to Buntingford, opened in 1863, closed 1964; Watford to Rickmansworth, opened in 1862, closed 1962; and Harpenden to Hemel Hempstead, opened in 1877, closed 1947.

Page 125   (above) *Wadesmill bridge, built in 1825;* (below) *iron bridge, c 1840,*
at Gadebridge Park, Hemel Hempstead

Page 126 (above) *Cow Roast lock on the Grand Union Canal at Wigginton, 382 ft above sea-level;* (below) *Grand Union Canal, Grove Park bridge, Watford*

But, a decade or more before the earliest of these lines was thought of, Cheshunt witnessed the opening of a 'truly excellent invention', than which, according to the contemporary *Register of Arts and Sciences* in a moment of verbal aberration, 'no mode of travelling can possibly be less free from danger'. This was a suspension trolleyway, a monorail, designed to carry not passengers but bricks from a Cheshunt brickfield to a wharf on the Lea Navigation about half a mile away. For the opening ceremony, however, a few trucks were 'elegantly constructed in the barouche style, the passengers sitting opposite each other', while bands played, flags fluttered, refreshments were served and a good time was had by all. This monorail was the invention of Henry Robinson Palmer who had built a similar one at the Deptford Victualling Yard. Drawn by a single horse, it consisted of seven or eight pairs of trucks balanced on each side of a stout timber rail shod with iron, along which a wheel attached to each pair of trucks conveyed them so smoothly 'as to be compared to the floating of boats in the stream of a river'. The wooden rail was supported by upright posts about 10 ft apart; 'under the rail and between a cleft of each of the posts are placed reverse wedges, which admit of a facile and almost instantaneous adjustment of the plane' to the undulations of the ground. At the point at which the monorail crossed a turnpike road both rail and supporting posts appear to have hinged back in a gate-like frame to allow the passage of road traffic. Opened in 1825, the monorail continued in use for some years but the date of its abandonment cannot be traced. It is not shown on a surveyor's map made soon after 1841; perhaps, on the other hand, he did not consider it relevant to the map's purpose and omitted it.

While in recent years British Railways have brought up to date certain stations along routes that are still open, they must also accept responsibility for at least three instances of destruction that are regrettable by the scale of railway values in Hertfordshire. The first is the demolition in 1966 of an 1838 ticket office at Tring, probably the surviving portion of a larger building, with pedimented entrance and pilastered side wall, unlike any other railway building in the county.

H

The second is the demolition of the handsome iron canopy, originally glass-covered, over both platform and track at Abbey Station, St Albans, on the St Albans–Watford branch line; it was removed in 1967 when the station became unstaffed. The third is the demolition in 1968 of the fine engine shed at Watford, built about 1858 though in part rebuilt somewhat later. Perhaps a matter for further regret is the recent encasing in cement of the graceful iron work of a railway bridge over the Grand Union Canal at Nash Mills, King's Langley. Various small warehouses and engine sheds of pleasing though not distinguished design have also vanished, and small items of equipment such as hand-operated cranes at Berkhamsted and Ware (the latter under a shingled canopy) are no longer there. However, at the time of writing there still remain a few items of interest to the industrial archaeologist—the 1842 three-storey station offices at Bishop's Stortford and the 1843 warehouse with fanlight windows at Ware (plate, page 143) are examples. At Hatfield a single-storey extension at the south end of the main station building, now used as offices, was originally Lord Salisbury's private waiting-room while his railway coach was being shunted into the adjacent bay. At Hatfield also the two staggered platforms are joined by an iron footbridge of which some of the supporting columns are topped by iron Corinthian capitals dating from the opening of the line in 1850; both there and at Hitchin the spandrels of the canopy arches are filled by a floral design of the same date. At Hertford East station, which replaced the 1843 one in 1888, there are two electric buffer lights carried on graceful fluted iron columns, about 6 ft in height, plainly taken from the original station (plate, page 143). Watford Junction, Watford High Street, Rickmansworth and Hitchin all have attractive iron canopies over their entrances, while brick porticos are found at Hertford East, Stanstead St Margaret's, Ware and other places; and characteristic 'Midland Railway Gothic' adorns Harpenden Central, St Albans City and Radlett.

Many stations along the former Great Eastern route to Bishop's Stortford and Cambridge are still of the pleasantly old-fashioned wooden type, often with an iron or concrete footbridge spanning a line now used by electrified units. But it is on some of the closed branch lines that the erstwhile charm of Hertfordshire railways can still be recalled in such insignificant little stations as Nast Hyde Halt, near Hatfield, or Mardock on the St Margaret's–Buntingford line, or in others consisting of no more than a single timber platform on stilts with a timber all-purpose office propped against a sturdy brick chimney. Many of these little stations are derelict or in sad process of becoming so; a few that are brick-built, notably along the old Hatfield–Hertford branch, have been converted into comfortable dwellings, either occupied by railway employees or sold to outsiders. There might seem scope for at least some others to follow their example.

No point in Hertfordshire reaches 1,000 ft above sea level; by far the greater part of the area is gentle undulating country of less than half that elevation. Little scope therefore exists for engineering enterprise of significance; but the county does in fact contain several items of interest. Let us follow each of the main lines northward from London, beginning with the old London & North Western out of Euston.

First, so far as Hertfordshire is concerned, come Bushey Arches over the Watford–London road, A411, at the south end of Watford. Consisting of five stone-faced arches of about 30 ft span and 25 ft height, they were originally built for two tracks in 1837 when the line was first opened; but in 1859 the necessity for a third track led to the building of a separate steel structure, some 18 ft wide, alongside, leaving a gap of about 7 ft between the two. In 1875 a fourth line was laid over this gap by fixing rolled steel joists from the parapet of the old viaduct to the third line structure. Some of the abutments were extended southward under the gap and the rails laid on longitudinal timbers over the joists. Extensive repairs and modernisation were undertaken in about 1960.

Immediately beyond Bushey Arches the line crosses the Colne by a five-arch brick viaduct, each arch having a span of about 40 ft and the middle one a height of about 45 ft, widened in 1859 and again in 1875. Watford Junction, just beyond this viaduct, was built in 1858 in place of the original 1837 one, which lay on the north side of a bridge carrying the Watford–St Albans road, A412; adjoining the bridge is a public house, the Leviathan, built in 1838 and named after an early locomotive. The line then enters Watford tunnel, 1 mile 57 yd in length, duplicated in 1874; it was necessitated by the refusal of the Earl of Essex to countenance a railway near his mansion of Cassiobury and cost many lives in the course of its building. The ornamental portals of the old tunnel are depicted in a well-known lithograph by J. C. Bourne. Thereafter the line runs along the valleys of the Gade and Bulbourne, crossing and recrossing both streams and the Grand Union Canal at several points. At Berkhamsted the station, built in 1875, replaced a former one, close to which the line had cut through part of the outer works of Berkhamsted Castle—a reminder that vandalism is not confined to the present day. At Berkhamsted too is a curious bridge, now carrying four tracks, of which one abutment makes a right-angled turn half-way through the bridge's width, thus giving a narrow entrance one on side and a wide one on the other. And finally at Tring the line enters Tring Cutting to pass through the Chiltern escarpment; it is 2½ miles long and with a depth of up to 60 ft. The 1½ million tons of soil from its excavation were used to create an embankment 6 miles long and of an average height of 30 ft at its Buckinghamshire end. A frequently reproduced lithograph by J. C. Bourne depicts an army of navvies working there.

On the old Midland Railway out of St Pancras the Elstree tunnel, half of which is in Middlesex, is 1,058 yd in length. Close together at St Albans two bridges may be noted. One, crossing the closed St Albans–Hatfield branch line which here ran in a cutting, has a remarkably graceful single semi-circular arch of brick, some 35 ft in height, in which four courses of brickwork are stepped progressively back to the arch rim. It is flanked by massive buttresses and of all Hertfordshire railway bridges is the most aesthetically pleasing. The other is a fine girder skew construction over the London road, A6; though with continuous brick abutments, it is in fact two bridges, each carrying two tracks, and separated by a gap of about 10 ft. A little higher up the line, to the south of Harpenden (Bowling Alley), is a skew brick bridge of different type; here both abutments and single arch carrying four tracks are ribbed in echelon to take the skew—a small girder bridge having similar echeloned abutments is on the old Great Northern line at Woolmer Green, north of Welwyn.

Out of King's Cross, the old Great Northern encountered a difficult bottleneck in Potters Bar tunnel, 1,210 yd long, which up to 1959, when it was duplicated, was built for only two tracks. A little north of Hatfield are a couple of strange bridges very close together, one over the Lea, the other spanning an accommodation road from Woodhall Farm. That over the Lea has three arches on its east side, five on its west; the other has five arches on its west side but only one on its east. Both date originally from 1850; the reason for the disparity between their two sides is the reconstruction in 1895 of the Hatfield–Wheathampstead–Luton branch.

It is about a mile north of Welwyn Garden City station that Hertfordshire's strongest claim to the attention of railway industrial archaeologists is seen: Welwyn viaduct (plate, page 144), also called Digswell Viaduct, over the Mimram valley—and close to the spot at which Charles Blondin, the tightrope walker, trained for his crossing of Niagara Falls in 1862. It is sometimes included among the great viaducts of England, but with dubious, though still arguable, justice. Of blue brick kilned on the spot, it consists of 40 arches of an average span of 40 ft, the highest being 100 ft above the river; its length is 1,560 ft in a straight line. It was designed by Lewis Cubitt and built by Thomas Brassey between 1848 and 1850; the first train to cross it is pictured in the *Illustrated London News* of 11 August in the latter year.

It is interesting to note in passing that the 1851 Census includes in Welwyn sixteen British subjects born in France, all railway workers or the wives or young families of railway workers. All had presumably been previously connected, directly or indirectly, with railway building in France. How many more had moved elsewhere since the opening of the line at Welwyn in the previous year it is, of course, impossible to guess.

Welwyn viaduct is the southern point of a couple of miles that still carry only two tracks; elsewhere there are now four. At the northern end of the viaduct is Welwyn North station; just beyond the station are two tunnels, 429 yd and 1,047 yd in length, the scene in 1866 of a fatal accident when three trains collided and caught fire in the shorter one. Immediately beyond is another viaduct of seven arches, the middle arch about 65 ft above a steep-sided ravine known as Robbery Bottom—a favourite lurking place during the seventeenth and eighteenth centuries for highwaymen and footpads on the Great North Road close by.

There is evidence to suggest that the railway company had originally entertained a plan, soon quashed by the opposition of local landowners, which envisaged taking the line via Welwyn and through the fairly easy terrain round Kimpton into the middle of Hitchin. The alternative that was adopted was the existing route through Stevenage and touching only the outskirts of Hitchin; but at Welwyn it involved, as has been seen, the building of two viaducts and the excavation of two tunnels. When in later years the company was forced to consider additional tracks, this difficult section presented problems that seemed permanently to deny a satisfactory solution. Only in 1898 was Parliamentary sanction obtained for an alternative —the construction of a loop line from Stevenage through Hertford to Wood Green, in the north of London. This line was opened from Wood Green to Cuffley, in the extreme south of Hertfordshire, in 1910 and over its full length in 1920; it embraces Hertfordshire's longest tunnel—Ponsbourne Tunnel, near Hatfield, 1 mile 920 yd in length, with five air shafts—and two fine seven-arch brick viaducts, one at Cuffley, the other over the Lea at Hertford.

On the old Great Eastern route out of Liverpool Street there are no features of much note. Between Stanstead Abbots and Sawbridgeworth it lies for the most part in Essex. The branch from Rye House to Hertford passes the 1843 goods shed at Ware already mentioned. At Hertford the original station at the bottom of Railway Street, after serving as goods terminal, was demolished in 1964.

Away from these principal routes two or three bridges call for cursory mention. At Slip End, Ashwell, on the Hitchin–Royston–Cambridge branch, is a three-arch bridge of which the middle segmented arch is very slightly lower in height than the outer ones and has, in addition, been reinforced by a semi-circular arch built inside it. On the outskirts of Hemel Hempstead, the now closed Harpenden–Hemel Hempstead branch crossed Queensway by a bridge of which the single arch, some 25 ft high, is amply buttressed and has massive arcaded wing walls; outside these wing walls pedestrian tunnels 9 ft high run under the embankment. And near Watford the Metropolitan Railway to Rickmansworth is carried at two points close together by girder bridges with brick abutments so large as almost to merit the name of viaducts—glaring contrasts to the score or more tiny red-brick bridges, having a mere 10 ft or 11 ft headroom under which the road dips steeply, that are found on several branch lines now trackless, leaving the bridges virtually the sole (and very charming) reminders of their existence.

POSTING BOXES

No less important than physical means of communication are those in writing, by word of mouth or over the air. Penny postage was introduced in 1840. Thereafter the rapidly increasing volume of industrial commercial and personal correspondence demanded drastic rethinking on all traditional channels of mail conveyance; no industrial archaeologist can fail to take account of the early posting boxes that replaced the receiving offices to which letters had formerly to be taken for despatch.

As is well known, it was Anthony Trollope, then a post office surveyor's clerk, who suggested in 1851 'a safe receptacle for letters' in the form of 'iron posts erected at the corners of roads'—they had already been successfully introduced in France. By 1853, after an experiment in Jersey, a few were set up in England, their number quickly growing and quickly changing in design as experience dictated. No early pillar boxes of any design, however, survive in Hertfordshire, though some certainly existed;[1] the earliest still to be seen, made by Handyside & Co, Derby and London, is outside the Town Hall, Hemel Hempstead. It belongs to the first (1878–83) of two types in which the words 'Post Office' and the royal cipher were inadvertently omitted; an example of the second type (1883–7) stands in Station Road, Harpenden, differentiated from the other only by a lower postal aperture. The next type (1887–1901) saw 'Post Office' and the royal cipher reinstated; there are seven examples of it in Hertfordshire—including one in an only recently developed area of Letchworth and one in the middle of an RAF station at Bovingdon. All posting boxes while they remain serviceable are liable to be moved from their original sites to new ones at the discretion of the Post Office.

Boxes of post-Victorian date are too common to merit special mention; but it may be added that relatively rare examples of the Edward VIII cipher can be seen on pillar boxes at Chorley Wood, Hertford, St Albans and Cuffley.

Victorian wall boxes, built into walls or brick pillars, are frequently met; there are rather more than eighty in Hertfordshire, though only in the small size; after 1861 successive types of wall box were made in two and sometimes three sizes, varying chiefly in width. Wall boxes were introduced at the beginning of 1858, made by Smith & Hawkes, Eagle Foundry, Birmingham. This foundry continued to make them until 1880; from then until 1965 they were made by W. T. Allen Ltd, London. Thus, since most boxes bear a visible maker's name (in others it is obliterated by layers of official red paint), 1880

---

[1] Two early pillar boxes, one of about 1855, the other of a few years later, are preserved—no longer, of course, in use—in the grounds of Colesgrove House, Cheshunt (TL333026).

is one landmark in their dating; another is 1871, when the original downshoot postal aperture, protected by a metal flap and, after 1859, by a hood as well, gave way to an upshoot one protected only by a hood. Closer dating may be obtained from such details as the shape and position of the enamelled notice and 'Next Collection' plates and of the escutcheon over the lock, the absence or presence of the words 'Letter Box' on the lower rim of the postal aperture, and so on. But the problem of dating can be bedevilled by later modification applied to existing boxes.

Hexton possesses the earliest wall box in Hertfordshire (plate, page 144), set up in 1860 (though now in the wall of a post office rebuilt about 1913); it is followed by another of the same type at Great Gaddesden in the next year. Both are 30 in high and 10 in wide. They have a pedimented top, below which is a hood bearing the words 'Post Office'. The small postal aperture under this hood has its metal flap, with the words 'Letter Box' on the lower rim of the aperture. The door is divided into three horizontal panels. The top one carries the royal cipher with crown and the words 'Cleared at'; in both the Hexton and the Great Gaddesden boxes the middle one is blank, as though a time or times of clearance had been impermanently painted or gummed there; the third contains the lock. Below that a large lower panel is an integral part of the box. On the bottom rim is 'Smith and Hawkes, Birmingham'.

In 1861 a new type, of which there are 17 examples in Hertfordshire, has the lock protected by an escutcheon. The pedimented top has gone, an enamelled plate for notices is bolted to the box, not fitted into a frame as it was to be later, and the door, which contains the 'Next Collection' plate, is lowered to enable the postman to clear the bottom of the box without having to grope blindly in the interior. Except for the substitution of a small upshoot for the previous downshoot aperture in 1871, the next two types, in 1871 and 1881 respectively, contain relatively minor changes.

The 1881 type was the last Victorian design. But in about 1960, as an economy measure, a number of these boxes, as well as boxes of later types, had their postal aperture enlarged to the full width of the box, with an impressive protective plate and hood moulded to it, giving them at first glance the appearance of a new type. On what principle, if any, the choice of boxes for adaptation was made is not known; there are six adapted boxes in Hertfordshire as against forty-three unadapted ones.

In 1896 the Post Office introduced a new form of posting box, apparently confined to thinly populated districts—the lamp box, strapped to lamp standards, telegraph poles or wooden posts; there are eight of them in Hertfordshire. With a domed top containing the words 'Letters Only', their postal aperture with hood is, as usual, small for present-day requirements. Below the aperture the whole front, which contains the notice and 'Next Collection' plates and a lock without escutcheon, forms the door, with the royal cipher at the bottom. There is a good deal of resemblance between them and the 1881 wall boxes, though without the embellishments of the latter. At their back is the maker's name, Handyside & Co, Derby and London.

All known Victorian posting boxes in Hertfordshire are listed in Appendix Three.

In the decade which saw the introduction of a penny post, the electric telegraph was first emerging as a potentially practical means of communication. But its earliest traceable connection with Hertford-shire—an indirect one—is lurid rather than soberly scientific. It concerns John Tawell, a much respected Quaker resident of Berkhamsted but also—unknown to his fellow townsmen—an ex-transport who had been convicted for forgery. Having returned to England and married advantageously in Berkhamsted, he some time later poisoned his mistress (his first wife's maid), whom he had installed not far off at Slough, Bucks; and having done so, made his way to London. Unfortunately for him, however, the crime was discovered very soon after he had left his mistress's house and the electric telegraph between Slough station and Paddington, opened by the Great Western Railway about a year previously, set to work. Tawell was picked up by detectives at Paddington, trailed back to Berkhamsted and arrested on his own doorstep. He was executed at Aylesbury, Bucks, in March 1845.

Railway companies early exploited it, though principally for their own purposes; several private telegraph companies were also formed. By 1867 St Albans had a telegraph office on Holywell Hill, though which company was concerned is not known. Three years later the Post Office acquired a monopoly of telegraph services in the United Kingdom; by 1878 telegraph offices, attached to post offices, were found in all Hertfordshire towns as well as in such apparently unlikely villages as Therfield, Barkway, Puckeridge, Much Hadham and Shenley. At Elstree an office was opened in Boreham Wood railway station.

Even at that date some competition to the telegraph was provided by the telephone, operated by a number of small private companies. It was not, however, until after these had amalgamated as the National Telephone Company in 1889 and the Post Office had taken over all trunk lines in 1892 that a public telephone service can be traced in Hertfordshire. In 1895 the National Telephone Company had a public call office at Bushey; four years later there were offices at Barnet, Berkhamsted, Hertford, Rickmansworth, St Albans, Ware, Watford and Waltham Cross, extended in the following half a dozen years to Bishop's Stortford, Harpenden and Hoddesdon.

As for the most recent form of communication, it may be noted that the BBC opened its transmitting station at Brookmans Park in October 1929. Some years later it was from a Post Office radio station at Smallford, near Colney Heath, that Government scientists received the first hints that led to the development of radar in 1933. The Second World War brought Service radio stations of several kinds to the county.

CHAPTER SIX

Industrial Watford 1800-1968

THIS outline of the development since 1800 of Hertfordshire's foremost industrial town utilises certain facts that have been already given in previous chapters, though they appear here, of course, in a different context. In his *Tour Through the Whole Island of Great Britain* (1724) Defoe describes Watford as 'a genteel market town, very long, having but one street'. That description, in much the same words, was adopted by county directories down to little more than a century ago. But off both sides of the street, which was about a mile in length, grew up innumerable courts and alleys approached through a gateway with a room above it, huddled, ill-built, crowded, insanitary, ensuring for the whole town a death rate above even the liberal average of the eighteenth and nineteenth centuries. Picturesque it assuredly was—but not a good place to live in, for all that it was the seat of a long established market, on a mail coach route from London to Birmingham and one or two cross-country routes as well, with Cassiobury, mansion of the Earl of Essex, on its doorstep and the Grove, where Lord Clarendon lived, close at hand. The published recollections of two Watfordians who could remember it in the early days of the nineteenth century speak of scrawny fowls scrabbling over the roadways, of watching the townsfolk carrying water from the communal pump in baskets suspended from their shoulders by a yoke, of stocks in the market place and the pound in St Albans Road, of a town apparently deserted after dark, of a night watchman patrolling the streets and crying the hour and the state of the weather. All these items could, of course, be matched elsewhere; they are given here merely as evidence of Watford's typical eighteenth-century market-town character. A local board, replacing the old parish vestry in 1850, certainly did something to improve sanitation,

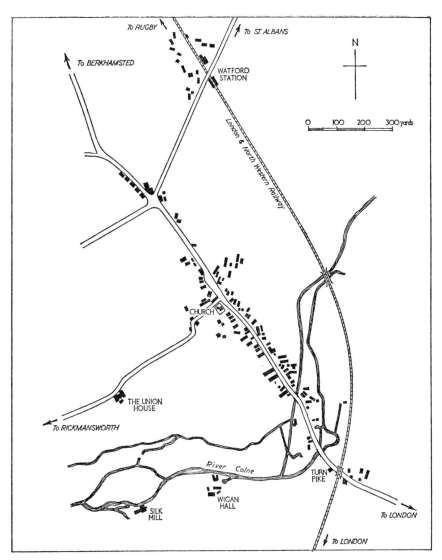

To RUGBY

To ST ALBANS

To BERKHAMSTED

WATFORD STATION

N

London & North Western Railway

0   100   200   300 yards

CHURCH

THE UNION HOUSE

To RICKMANSWORTH

River Colne

TURN PIKE

WIGAN HALL

SILK MILL

To LONDON

To LONDON

Watford town in 1849

water supply, street lighting and so on; but it was only under an urban district council after 1894 that most of the ancient plague spots fell before new standards of social amenity. Even so, their last vestiges survived until the erection of a large covered market behind High Street in 1928—that is to say, after Watford had become a municipal borough six years previously.

Until relatively recent times the parish of Watford was 10,777 acres and included not only the town but also the hamlet of Cashio (north of the St Albans and Rickmansworth roads), Oxhey, Leavesden and the estate of Garston, which even in 1880 Cussans' *History of Hertfordshire* (Cashio Hundred) could call 'a small hamlet sparsely scattered on both sides of the St Albans Road'. In the 1801 Census the total parish population was given as 3,530, the bulk of whom it is safe to assume lived in the town. St Albans and Hertford were rather larger, Hemel Hempstead of about the same size, Hitchin and Cheshunt rather smaller. Agriculture was the preponderant employment but such home or home workshop occupations as straw plaiting, wood turning and candle making were also carried on. A brewery, a flour mill and a coachbuilder provided other employment; and there was at least one silk mill, at that date thirty or more years old. Not far away were two paper mills—Hamper Mill, near the south end of the town, and the small Bushey Mill, the latter continuing at work until about 1820. But how many hands these various enterprises employed can only be guessed. Not many, certainly.

The opening of the Grand Junction Canal in 1800 might appear at first sight to have offered Watford an industrial opportunity, providing as it did a second traffic artery to London in one direction and to the Midlands in the other. In the immediate neighbourhood of Watford moreover were one or two wharves along the canal banks. The canal, however, was separated from the town by the large park surrounding the Earl of Essex's mansion of Cassiobury, a sacrosanct barrier, and a proposed Watford and St Albans branch canal was never constructed. On the river Colne, which flowed through the lower part of Watford and was connected with the canal near Rickmansworth, were the two paper mills, the silk mill and the flour mill; but the Colne, small and somewhat erratic, can at best have been useful solely as a source of power, not as a channel for transport. Between 1801 and 1841, a span of forty years, Watford population less than doubled, which, when natural increase is taken into account, suggests trifling, if any, industrial influx. The 1831 Census records only 412 'families chiefly engaged in trade, manufacture or handicrafts' as against 397 in agriculture and 287 described as 'all other families'. Nor do contemporary directories, selective though they are in their listing of names, suggest the incoming of industries—except for two cases. In 1816 James Hugh Perry applied to the Justices of Liberty of St Albans for a licence to set up a printing press; and in about 1827 George Tidcombe established an iron foundry and engineering workshop. A private gas company was formed in 1834.

In 1837 the London & Birmingham Railway linked Watford with London and in 1838 with Birmingham, providing a third artery of communication. In the twenty years between 1841 and 1861 the population rose by roughly one quarter—the influence of the railway seems, at first at least, to have been no greater than that of the canal. A steep rise in population of rather more than one half between 1861 and 1871 is attributed 'largely' by the *Victoria County History of Herts* and also by Cussans to the coming during that decade of the Metropolitan Asylum for Pauper Imbeciles, the St Pancras Industrial Schools and the London Orphan Asylum; but though they no doubt contributed an appreciable proportion, there were railway improvements in 1857 and considerable extensions of residential building in the town, which almost certainly contributed as much or more.[1] The three institutions apart, how many of the new residents were employed locally, how many worked elsewhere in Hertfordshire (a branch line to St Albans had been opened in 1858 and to Rick-

---

[1] In a note to the writer, Mr Rex Wailes says: 'In the 1860s and 1870s, in order to build up Watford, the LNWR offered a free first class pass to go with houses costing more than a certain fairly large sum. The pass went with the house, whoever owned it. Mr George Wailes, who bought a house in St Andrews Road in the late 1860s, had a free first class pass to Euston for the unexpired 17 years of its 21 years' validity.

mansworth in 1862) and how many were commuters to London (for
Watford by that time enjoyed a good rail service to the city) it is
impossible to determine. What is noticeable is an increase in the
number of builders and builders' merchants in the town, two banks
in place of the former one, two printers, two boot and shoe manufacturers, a second iron and brass founder, a sugar-manufacturing
depot, a ginger beer maker and the Steam Mineral Water Co Ltd.
The town also had its Co-operative Store and, in 1855, its own newspaper.

It is, however, in the twenty years after 1881 that the rate of increase quickens, though it must be borne in mind that the greater the
population the greater will be the natural increase. Between 1881,
when the population was 15,506, and 1901, when it was 29,327, it
roughly doubled. The number of printing firms rose by 1898 to eight;
and there were also two iron founders, two firms of engineers, several
electrical and motor engineers, a weighing machine manufacturer, a
'domestic machine depot', a piano and musical instrument manufacturer, a 'leaded lights and stained glass window manufacturer',
photographic plate and paper makers and the Singer Manufacturing
Co, makers of sewing machines. The number of merchandising, as
distinct from manufacturing, firms also rose sharply and there were
such fringe urban adjuncts as a billposting company. But at the same
time—relics of earlier days—there were three breweries, four coach-
builders and a straw hat factory. As for the well-established papermaking industry at Hamper Mill, it had been supplemented as long
ago as 1830 by John Dickinson's mill at Croxley, Rickmansworth,
which employed a steadily growing number of Watford hands; and
there was also in the town a manufacturing stationer. The silk
industry at Rookery Mill had, however, ceased in 1881.

A glimpse of at least some working conditions at that period is
given by A. Barnard in his *Noted Breweries of the United Kingdom*
(1889–91), when he speaks of the Benskin brewery, near the middle
of the town, as 'surrounded by gardens, trees and parklike lands' and
of the Georgian mansion adjoining, now the brewery offices, 'with

(above) *Ware station goods shed, built in 1843;* (below) *buffer lights at Hertford East station, c 1843*

Page 144   (above) *Welwyn viaduct, built in 1850;* (below) *1860 posting box, Hexton*

its background of flower gardens, lawns and stately trees'. A print of Rookery Mill, on the town outskirts, shows it standing in open country. On the other hand, many industries were crammed into already congested areas, chock-a-block with dwelling houses and difficult of access.

Nor was Watford alone in being invaded by more and more industry; Hemel Hempstead was expanding also. Between the two towns the charming Gade valley, along which both railway and canal ran, increasingly presented itself as a potential industrial area as the twentieth century dawned. Luckily Hunton Bridge and Abbot's Langley formed a buffer to strictly Watford expansion, though residential expansion within the borough has by now taken place right up to their boundary; particularly between the two World Wars much of the Gade valley became steadily filled by a number of small industries, from gravel digging upwards, and by some larger ones as well, that seriously impaired without quite destroying its character. Regional planning, then in its infancy, failed to impose seemliness upon industry left to its own devices; today the valley has become so tatty, shabby and disfigured by hotchpotch building as to rank as an eyesore in an otherwise extremely attractive region.

By 1911 Watford's population had leaped to 40,939. During the period of the First World War it slackened again; but between 1921 (45,910) and 1931 (56,799) it once more rose sharply by some 11,000. Kelly's Directory for 1929 shows how much wider the variety of industry had become. It comprised 12 firms of printers, 4 photo engravers and 1 printing ink manufacturer. In other fields there were 16 firms of engineers, 10 electrical engineers or battery makers, 21 motor engineers and body builders, 8 firms of food manufacture or processing, 6 of joinery and woodwork, 4 boot and shoe manufacturers, 4 manufacturing chemists, 4 haulage contractors and many miscellaneous industries—water softener manufacturer, wire brush manufacturer, switch gear manufacturer, typewriter supplies manufacturer, chain and link fence manufacturer and so on. In all, some ninety industrial establishments operated in the town—with, it was

I

officially stated in 1932, only three factory chimneys, electric power, first installed by the Urban District Council in 1902, being almost universal. The opening of a Watford bypass (A41) in 1927 not only eased intolerable traffic congestion in the narrow High Street but also offered to industry a large and unencumbered new area.

The threshold of the Second World War saw a further expansion, with 18 firms of printers already established and, among new-comers, makers of biscuits, table and optical glass, implement handles, scent, cash registers, perambulators, paint, rubber hose, dressed leather and furniture—in addition, of course, to existing engineering firms of all kinds, food producing firms, breweries, wood turners and three blacksmiths (of whom there were still two in 1966). As soon as the war started a small Service airfield was created on what had previously been earmarked for a public playing field at Leavesden. It was subsequently taken over by the De Havilland Aircraft Co Ltd and later by Bristol Siddeley Ltd, largely for work on aircraft engines; it has been occupied since 1967 by Leavesden Air Servicing Ltd.

In the twenty years between 1931 and the next Census in 1951 Watford's population rose by roughly 16,000 to 73,130, but between 1951 and 1961 by only 2,500, to 75,630. It is not possible to give reliable up-to-date figures of employment; in 1961 there were 10,194 engaged in printing, publishing and paper making, 6,343 in engineering and electrical work, 6,760 in aircraft and vehicles and 2,914 in the food and drink industries, including brewing. The total employed in all forms of manufacture was 33,288; in very marked contrast to a century and a half earlier, only 555 were occupied in agriculture. It should be noted, however, that Board of Trade re-strictions on the establishment of new industries in south-west Herts may modify increases in the future.

The most striking development in local industries is that of print-ing; indeed, Watford has now earned the title of the greatest concen-tration of printers in the world. It is therefore important to sketch, however discursively, one or two salient points in the development of the industry since James Hugh Perry set up his press in 1816. He was still in the town in 1822, when he ran into trouble for not receiving an apprentice back into his service.

It is generally said that John Peacock either succeeded or entered into competition with him in 1823; but only in 1827 did Peacock apply for a licence under an Act of 1798, stating that he 'has a printing press and types, which he proposes to use for printing in his house, situate in the centre of the town'. Is 'proposes to' the operative phrase or was he applying for a renewal? At all events, his business prospered with the slow development of the town and he is recorded in 1855 as publishing the *Watford Weekly Advertiser*. About this— Watford's first newspaper—however, nothing whatever is known and no copy now exists; it was his son, Samuel Alexander Peacock, who issued in 1863 the first newspaper that still continues, the *Watford Observer*.

Of its four pages, three containing political and general news were printed in London, by what appears to have been a kind of syndicated service distributing to a number of provincial newspapers, who filled the fourth with local news and advertisements. For this fourth page Peacock used a handsomely decorative Columbian press dating from 1820; after remaining in service for proofing until 1955, it is now preserved by the Watford Corporation. In 1865, however, the first cylinder press was introduced, still hand-operated but quicker and more efficient than its predecessor. By 1880, when the paper had been enlarged to six pages, the whole issue was printed in the Watford works, with supplements whenever the pressure of news demanded. The buying up of several smaller news-sheets in the early part of this century necessitated further increase of size and modernisation of plant; more recently the 32-page paper was printed on a 90-ton rotary press, for which the web off-set litho method was substituted in 1968. Successive generations of the Peacock family remained in control until 1961.

The *Watford Observer* is, in fact, a latecomer among early (though not necessarily surviving) Hertfordshire newspapers; even in its own district the _Hemel Hempstead Gazette_ preceded it by five years. In Watford itself it was to meet competition from various short-lived rivals, permanently after 1887 from the _West Herts Post and Watford News Letter_, now the _Watford and West Herts Post_. But, both as Watford's first continuing newspaper and as the product of a firm that is certainly by far the oldest of its kind in the town, it is not to be ignored by industrial archaeologists.

Earlier paragraphs in this chapter have shown the slowly increasing number of printing firms during the nineteenth century. It is therefore surprising to learn from the 1891 Census that in all Hertfordshire, not in Watford alone, there were only 357 males and 8 females engaged in the printing industry, plus 16 males in lithography and 2 typecutters; at that date more than a dozen Hertfordshire newspapers, big and small, were in weekly production and the demands of commerce and industry were accelerating enormously. It is, indeed, only in the last half-century that Watford has achieved its present dominating position in the industry, largely because of the part it played in the development of colour printing and colour photogravure.

Seventy or so years ago colour printing was still something of a novelty to be exploited both technically and commercially. In 1903 Bemrose-Dalziel Ltd, an amalgamation of the Dalziel Foundry, London, and Bemrose & Co of Derby, who already had a printing works in the town, established themselves there as four-colour printers—the first firm in England to undertake multi-colour printing on a big scale and soon attracting the attention of the large and progressive fashion journal house of Weldon and Co Ltd. Five years later, however, Bemrose-Dalziel sold out to Waterlow Bros and Layton, later Waterlow & Sons Ltd. The work hitherto obtained from Weldon was taken over by two already existing Watford firms, Andre & Sleigh (owned by Cassell & Co, the London publishers) and the Acme Engraving Co, who amalgamated under the title of Andre & Sleigh and set up a second colour press at Bushey, which specialised in photogravure work. In 1914 Andre & Sleigh and the Bushey

Colour Press themselves amalgamated with the Anglo-Engraving Co Ltd and became the Sun Engraving Co Ltd in 1918. In 1934 the Sun acquired a controlling interest in the highly esteemed Rembrandt Intaglio Printing Co Ltd of Lancaster, photogravure printers, which had been established in 1893 and now moved lock, stock and barrel to Watford.

The man by whose vast technical knowledge, inventive flair and organising ability these developments were largely made possible was David Greenhill of Watford. It was he whom Harvey Dalziel first approached in 1903, who was the active and researching spirit in Andre & Sleigh and the Bushey Colour Press, who engineered both the specialised aspects and much of the financial side of subsequent amalgamations and who remained managing director of the Sun Engraving Co Ltd until his death in 1947. The friendly advice and help that he was invariably willing to give to firms other than his own is gratefully remembered by many of them; he was indefatigable in promoting the welfare of the industry and of those who earned their livelihood by it; and to call him the fairy godfather of today's printing industry in Watford is not, by those who knew him, regarded as too fanciful a title.

From the 1920s the Sun Engraving Co was printing mass-circulation magazines as well as many specialist colour photogravure productions of high quality. In the latter field it could draw freely on the accumulated research and experience of its parent firms; in the former its most spectacular success was the printing of the phenomenally popular *Picture Post* after 1936. By 1939 it was printing magazines with a total circulation of over 6,250,000 and employing 2,000 hands working in shifts from midnight on Sunday to 10 pm on Saturday. During the Second World War almost its whole organisation was turned to coping with the innumerable demands of the British and Allied Governments. After the war it was reorganised under the title of Sun Printers Ltd, a component of the British Printing Corporation.

In the 1920s and early 1930s it had undertaken a large amount of work for Odhams Ltd of London; but in 1936 Odhams built their own premises at Watford—a blow to the Sun luckily mitigated by the success of *Picture Post* in the same year. The new Odhams works consisted at first of a capacious single-storey building on the recently opened Watford by-pass; twenty years later this was enlarged to four storeys and additional buildings, the most conspicuous feature being a tower with copper-covered lantern 180 ft high. During the Second World War Odhams printed gigantic quantities of propaganda material for the British and Allied Governments and for various liberation forces—their highspot was the printing of the millions of leaflets scattered over France at the time of the D-day landings—as well as relinquishing part of their floor space to the Ministry of Aircraft Production. Today their eleven multi-unit rotary presses turn out over 7,000,000 copies of various magazines, colour supplements for the *New York Times* and the pre-printed colour portions of national newspapers. There are also large letterpress and bindery departments.

The year of Odhams' arrival saw the departure from Watford of Waterlow & Sons Ltd, who, as stated above, had taken over Andre & Sleigh in 1908 but did not establish works in the town until 1915. It was there that they were engaged chiefly in printing postage and revenue stamps; their earliest claim to notice at Watford, however, was the reprinting in 1915 of the whole first issue of £1 and 10s Treasury notes—the famous Bradburys—on paper less susceptible to the attention of forgers, a danger both discerned and rectified by David Greenhill.

As the prestige of its earlier printing houses spread, so did Watford attract during the inter-war period more and more firms seeking the benefit of its already high repute in the industry, lower rents and rates than in London, a pool of skilled labour, easy communications and pleasant surroundings for their people. The London blitz of 1940 brought others and a few have arrived more recently; in 1964 there were, in all, 32 firms in Watford itself and 9 in the immediately surrounding area, the majority working for London publishers and advertising agencies or for the Government. An atmosphere of friendly competition appears to pervade them all, faced as they are by the two giants, Odhams Ltd and Sun Printers Ltd. It is, however, doubtful whether both giants combined could show a bigger labour force than the total of all other printers in the area.

Meanwhile, a Watford imprint is to be seen not only on a great many glossy and non-glossy magazines but also on innumerable other forms of publication all over the world; and it is probable that no town anywhere can surpass the quality of its colour plate printing.

Two other Watford firms, still active, date back to the earliest days of the town's industrial development. They are the Watford Engineering Works Ltd and Benskin's Brewery Ltd. The development of the former is related to the growth of local papermaking.

About 1827 George Tidcombe set up in Watford as iron founder and engineer—one directory calls him also a millwright. A friend of the engineer, Bryan Donkin (see page 56), who had been associated with the Fourdrinier brothers in their experiments in papermaking machinery, Tidcombe had executed some of their early models and after their bankruptcy continued in the same line, though lack of immediate demand prevented him, of course, from devoting himself to it entirely. Yet by the 1830s he was building Fourdrinier-type machines for John Dickinson at Apsley and Nash Mills and for Hamper Mill, Watford; other orders followed as papermakers all over the country came to adopt the new techniques. His partners, Strudwick and later Brewer, dying in fairly quick succession, he carried on the business alone and in face of newly established general engineering competition in the town until his death, exporting during his lifetime papermaking machines to Belgium, France and Russia. Under his son, another George, however, it fell on evil days; in 1886 young George became manager of the Patent Strainer Plate Co Ltd, afterwards the Colne Valley Iron Foundry, leaving the Tidcombe firm to be restarted by Henry J. Rogers, who maintained its previous character in the manufacture of papermaking machinery. In 1911 it became the Watford Engineering Works Ltd. Though its present premises are new, they stand on the site of Tidcombe's original workshop alongside the Colne, exporting up-to-date Fourdrinier-type machines, much other papermaking equipment and the products of general engineering to between thirty-five and forty countries, as well as satisfying a large home demand.

In all market towns of great age, brewing ranked as an industry, however primitive, from the first emergence of the common brewer in the later Middle Ages. It is heard of at Watford in 1619 in the person of John Day; in 1635 there was a Swan Inn brewing its own beer, though whether it was the present house of that sign (rebuilt in 1957) cannot be said—in the nineteenth century three Swans in Watford were in licence simultaneously. By 1750 the town certainly had its brewery, the Cannon Brewery, already in the hands of the Dyson family, its holders for rather more than another century. But at any rate in their later days—a measure of Watford's growth—the Dysons were not without competition; in 1855 there were two more breweries, Whittingstall (some half-century old) with a large, Roate with a small one. Nine years later, Dyson still being the principal, there were three more—Sedgwick, who had replaced Whittingstall in 1862, Roate and Healey. Attached to each of these breweries were several malthouses, whose number was further swelled by two or three owned by the Stanmore (Middlesex) brewery of Clutterbuck.

In 1868, however, Dyson sold to Joseph Benskin, of Leicestershire birth, formerly a licensee and hotel keeper in London and a man of immense business capacity. With an immediate start on the reconstruction of the old brewery buildings, there followed the steady extension of the family-owned Benskin firm—the purchase, first of Roate, then of Healey about 1898, of Sedgwick in 1924, of Wells's Lion Brewery, which had been established in 1890, at about the period of the Second World War, and of half a dozen or more others outside the town. The number of licensed houses under their control rose steadily to several hundred, chiefly in West Hertfordshire; indeed, in many respects they came to enjoy almost a regional monopoly. But in 1957, when they had long since become a limited liability company with a close connection of the Benskin family as chairman, they were absorbed into the vast organisation of Ind Coope Ltd. Benskin's Watford brewery still, however, brews under its own name in premises covering 13,000 sq ft, with plans for further expansion.

About Watford's present status as Hertfordshire's leading industrial town there is no doubt. But other places—Letchworth, Welwyn Garden City, Stevenage, Boreham Wood, Hemel Hempstead, St Albans, the Lea valley, to name the chief ones, are steadily expanding their industrial intake and in the aggregate of their production certainly come near to equalling, if not surpassing, it. For all Watford's wide range of production, it has little cause for complacency; potential rivals are on every hand. A massive printing industry alone has so far ensured its supremacy in the Hertfordshire industrial scene.

PART TWO

Gazetteer

SITES mentioned in the text, except those of completely modern importation into the county, are included in this Gazetteer, along with additional entries of interest. All have been visited by the author fairly recently during the time of writing, but so rapidly is Hertfordshire changing that alteration or demolition is fairly certain since then to have overtaken some of them.

Disappointingly, the Grand Union Canal provides only a handful of entries. Few Hertfordshire railway stations are noteworthy; and of its several hundred road, waterway and railway bridges the majority exhibit no point of special interest. Half a dozen of the county's earliest milestones and its earliest posting box appear under their place names but complete lists of milestones and Victorian posting boxes are given in Appendices. Another Appendix lists Hertfordshire's London Coal Duty boundary markers. Ordnance Survey grid references are given for many of the items.

ANSTEY

Village pump. TL 403325; see page 94.

ARDELEY

Village pump. TL 308272; see page 93.
Windmill. Cromer (TL 300286); see page 52.

ASHWELL

Maltings. None now operating. (1) behind Digswell Manor, High Street, about 1800; (2) near cemetery, 1911; (3) west end of village, now village hall, about 1890; (4) at Ashwell brewery.

Mill. Partly collapsed about 1960 but grain store is now a Boy

Scout headquarters and the millhouse is occupied. No wheel. Working in 1839 and until early this century.

Railway bridge. Slip End (TL 283371); see page 133.

AYOT ST LAWRENCE

Wellhead gear. Simple direct-lift gears, partly wood, partly iron, in Cloacina Cottage (TL 198167) and Forge Cottage (TL 198166). Cottages probably eighteenth century.

BALDOCK

Maltings. Three still operating: (1) Seven Roes, off High Street, early nineteenth century, with furnace by H. S. King, Nailsworth, Glos; (2) Lion, Mansfield Road, with barley store on High Street, possibly late eighteenth century, tamped chalk floor, furnace by H. S. King; (3) Bygrave, Royston Road, two large maltings built 1884–98, one having two kilns, the other three, Suxé anthracite furnaces.

Four not operating: (1) behind no 41 High Street, now private house; (2) no 16B Hitchin Street, now private house; (3) no 33 Hitchin Street, now furniture store, much altered; (4) corner of White Horse Street and Clothall Road, now manufacturing chemist's premises, having two dismantled kilns, one with wire mesh flooring, the other with hair plaster lining.

Brewery. Behind Church Street. Present buildings probably about 1840, built by Steed & Oliver, but brewing on site earlier and continuing until 1938. Empty, but yard occupied by scrap merchant. No gear.

Silk mill. Kayser-Bondor Ltd; see pages 63, 70.

Coaching inn. George and Dragon, in existence in 1591 and said to have been a favourite with travelling Quakers. Extensive stabling but never Baldock's leading coaching inn, though the largest now surviving.

BARKWAY

Milestones. TL 385357 and TL 393369; see page 110 and Appendix Two.

BARLEY

Milestones. TL 397382 and TL 402398; see page 110 and Appendix Two.

BAYFORD

Bridge. Carrying side road at Roxford, TL 309109, dated 1838.

BERKHAMSTED

Malting. Castle Street. Probably mid-nineteenth century, built for Foster's brewery, now demolished; much altered and in various occupations.

Mill. Castle Mill, built 1895, now offices.

Water works. Engineer's house, 1864, of former Berkhamsted Water Company in High Street.

Turnpike post. SP 990079; iron, about 2 ft high, oval, immediately in front of building, inscribed 'Sparrows Herne Trust'. Purpose unknown; others at Tring (SP 919112) and Watford (TL 118955).

Coaching inn. King's Arms, established very early in eighteenth century. Stabling for 40 horses in 1890. Post office in eighteenth and first half of nineteenth centuries.

Canal. Rose Cottage bridge has iron girders bearing date 1889; Pix bridge with girders marked G. Deeley, Bilston; see page 121.

Railway station. On embankment with access by steps from yellow-brick booking and other offices at street level; see page 130. South of station a yellow-brick goods shed, probably 1837, adjoining site of former station at end of Castle Street. Bridge at south end of station; see page 130.

Ashridge. On site of medieval monastery, which after 1604 became the home of the Earls and Dukes of Bridgewater. The Canal Duke planned its rebuilding but the work was carried out after 1808 under his successor, the seventh Earl, by James Wyatt and Sir Jeffrey Wyatville. For description of horse-drive pumping gear over medieval well see page 96.

Joinery equipment. East & Son Ltd, Gossoms End; see page 16.

Includes bandsaw by Greenwood, Batley, Leeds, 1861; lathe by A. Ransom & Co, Ipswich; and bandsaw by Noble & Collier, London. *Repair depot.* Established in 1870 by Cooper McDougall & Robertson Ltd for their sheep-dip manufactury. Still in use: lathe, drill press, filter press by S. H. Johnson, Stratford East (no 539), bending rolls, leg vice. A circle cutter by Sibley & Son, Ashton-under-Lyne, 1847, formerly in the firm's possession, has been accepted by the Science Museum, South Kensington.

BISHOP'S STORTFORD

Maltings. Two still operating: (1) South Mill Road, three maltings, 1843, 1856, 1897; (2) Station Road, three maltings, one 1819, two modern.

Fifteen not operating: (1) Bridge Street, part of large block of maltings working until 1938, now builders' merchants' premises; (2) Dane Street, small, nineteenth century, now garage and repair shop; (3) Beech Mills, three mid-nineteenth-century maltings now part of mill premises; (4) Dell Lane, small weatherboarded, base of kiln used as paint shop in builder's store; (5) Gas Works Lane, probably mid-nineteenth century, now Eastern Gas Board store; (6) no 112 Hadham Road, now dwelling house but retaining dome of kiln; (7) no 19 Hockerill Street, built about 1800 but greatly altered, now business premises; (8) no 25 Hockerill Street, greatly altered; (9) no 27 Hockerill Street, probably early nineteenth century but possibly rather before, much cut up into workshops and flats, owned by Herts County Council and demolition possible on redevelopment of area; (10) Hockerill Street, south side, probably about 1860, now Eastern Electricity Board store; (11) Stanstead Road, late nineteenth century on site of an earlier malting, now furniture store and show rooms; (12) London Road, Hockerill, late nineteenth century but character almost completely lost, occupied by manufacturers of scientific instruments; (13) South Mill Yard, three large maltings, now in poor condition, timber store; (14) Station Road, greatly altered, now engineering workshop; (15) Windhill, Kiln Cottage, malting on site from late seventeenth to late nineteenth century, now private house retaining dome of kiln.

Mills. (1) Beech Mills, formerly Town Mill, rebuilt 1935 except for early nineteenth-century lodge at gate, still working on animal food-stuffs; (2) South Mill, weatherboarded on brick base, with wharf to Stort and brick engine house, milling until 1955 and now furniture store.

Gas holder. See page 88.

Railway station. See page 128.

Coaching inn. Though not on the Hockerill Trust road, the George was much used as a coach halt. Of late medieval foundation, it once had its own malthouse. Henry Gilbey, father of Sir Walter Gilbey, distiller, drove a coach daily from the George to London in the 1820s.

BOREHAM WOOD

Motion pictures. Boreham Wood is to be remembered as the home of Ideal Pictures Ltd in 1910. The cinematograph industry is still represented there but today its industries are far more various.

BOVINGDON

Malting. Bourne End, near Pix Farm (TL 019066); see page 37.

Mill. Bourne End. Brick-built and working until 1938. Wheel driven by cut from Grand Union Canal.

Canal bridge. TL 026064; see page 121.

BRAUGHING

Malting. One wall remains between Malting Lane and a garden on the site of an old malting operating from before 1860 to about 1900.

Mill. Gatesbury (TL 393239). Mill demolished in 1906 but small eighteenth-century millhouse survives, as well as a sluice and some early nineteenth-century buildings. A corn and fulling mill in 1636.

Village pump. See page 93.

Bridge. (TL 392248). Carrying B1368 over river Quin. Rebuilt 1937 but has old stone plaque 'Built in 1769 by William Edwards'.

K

BROOKMANS PARK

Estate. A large privately developed estate, entirely residential, begun at the period of the First World War.

Radio. BBC transmitting station, 400 ft above sea level, opened for radio October 1929, replacing London 2LO station. Experiments in television from March 1930. See Asa Briggs: *History of Broadcasting in the United Kingdom* (vol 1, 1961). Still has in reserve the original Marconi 50 kW regional type transmitter.

Horse trough (?) (TL 261035). In hedge alongside A1000. Stone, semi-circular, concave, about 2½ ft in diameter, with small pipe protruding from the base. A few lines of inscription are illegible. Might have been an eighteenth-century drinking fountain or horse trough.

BROXBOURNE

Mill. (TL 372068). See page 51.

New River. Pumping station (TL 374076) 1887. Bridges: south of Station Road (TL 371070); Mill Lane (TL 371068) 1841; see page 101.

Bridge. Adjoining station, over railway, river Lea and New River; see page 114.

Terra cotta works. (TL 373071). See page 80.

BUNTINGFORD

Mill. Aspenden (TL 363289). A small mill and dwelling house under a single thatched roof. Frame for wheel, mill race dried up. Working until about 1895, having been in hands of one family since seventeenth century. The same family also had a windmill at TL 369294, burnt down in 1905.

Village pump. See page 93.

Railway station. (TL 364288). Terminus of St Margaret's–Buntingford branch.

Bridges. (1) Aspenden (TL 363285), over river Rib, 1878; (2) two miles south of town, at TL 379263, over railway; see page 116.

BUSHEY

Water works. Colne Valley Water Co have large red-brick pumping station, 1873, with typical decorative chimney of the period; see page 97.

Horse trough. (TQ 145945). See page 112.

Bridge. Bushey Arches, carrying main line of former London and North Western Railway; see page 129.

CHESHUNT

Malting. A warning to industrial archaeologists: the Maltster's Arms public house was renamed about 1955 by a new licensee, Stanley Maltster; formerly the Railway Arms.

Gas works. Waltham Cross. Gas holder 1880, the oldest in Herts; see page 87.

New River. Pumping station, Canada Lane, Turnford (TL 364049), with Boulton & Watt engine; see page 100. Bridge at Flamstead End (TL 354036); see page 101.

Bridges. Three small road bridges can be dated: TL 364048 carrying A10 over Turnford Brook, pre-1872; TL 371004, carrying A121 over Small Lea, 1833; TL 368004 carrying A121 over stream, 1873.

Coaching inn. The Falcon, in existence in 1617 but rebuilt 1887. Opposite, the Old Four Swans, with gallows sign, older but closed 1965.

CHORLEYWOOD

Papermaking. Solesbridge Mill (TQ 042970), operating 1746–1902, now rearing trout and fancy fishes.

Wellhead gear. ¾ mile from Chorleywood House (TQ 039975), which it served; see page 95.

CODICOTE

Mill. Fulling mill (TL 226169); see page 77.

COLLIERS END

Lime kiln. TL 370202; see page 20.

COLNEY HEATH

Windmill. (TL 242031). Tower mill probably built about 1862 and working until early 1900s. No cap, sails or gear and now used as a workshop.

COLNEY STREET

Aviation. Handley Page Aviation Ltd were established here at the time of the Second World War; see page 26.

COTTERED

Village pump. TL 318295 (demolished 1969); see pages 93, 94.

CROXLEY GREEN

Windmill. (TQ 067953). Tower mill, built 1820. No cap, sails or gear and now a dwelling house.
Wellhead gear. (TQ 070966). At Croxley House; see page 95.
Horse trough. TQ 069953; see page 112.

CUFFLEY

Viaduct. TL 306017; see page 132.

ELSTREE

Tunnel. Elstree tunnel on old Midland Railway main line, half in Middlesex, TQ 197948–TQ 193953, length 1,058 yd, built 1868, duplicated 1895, one air shaft to each tunnel; see page 130.

ESSENDON

Mill. (TL 275097). Mill possibly eighteenth century, house might be seventeenth century. Ceased working about 1925. No wheel. Now wholly a private house.

FLAMSTEAD

Wellhead gear. Bonners Farm (TL 069168); see page 94.

FROGMORE, ST ALBANS

Mill. (TL 150024) Moor Mill; see page 51.

FURNEUX PELHAM

Malting and brewery. Brewery built by William Rayment in 1860; see page 46; has nineteenth-century equipment and also a malting.

GREAT AMWELL

New River. Emma's Well was one of the two original headsprings of the New River, 1608, now charmingly laid out and cared for. There are three pumping stations: Amwell Hill (TL 367127), built 1847; Amwell End (TL 361139) and Amwell Marsh (TL 367124). Bridges over the New River are at TL 366132 and TL 372216; see page 101.

GREAT GADDESDEN

Mill. Noke Mill (TL 043097), nineteenth-century mill, now disused, with wheel; seventeenth-century miller's house in poor condition.

Bridges. TL 040103 and TL 036105; see page 113.

Posting box. TL 027111; see page 135.

HARPENDEN

Donkey wheel. Annables Farm, Kinsbourne Green (TL 101156); see page 95.

Bridge. Bowling Alley; see page 131.

Gas works. See page 88.

Railway. Central Station, 1868.

HATFIELD

New Town. Designated a government-sponsored New Town in 1948, having same Development Corporation as Welwyn Garden City. Now under New Towns Commission.

Malting. Behind garage in middle of old town, probably late nineteenth century, formerly belonging to Pryor Reid's brewery, which closed in 1920.

Mills. (1) Mill Green Mill (TL 240097), built 1762, working until 1911, now private house; (2) Cecil Saw Mill, built 1830, working until about 1884, since then sawmill to Cecil Estates.

Papermaking. (TL 239100). Mill operating from before 1672 to 1838, burnt down 1883; but papermaker's eighteenth-century house remains; see page 55.

Horse trough. TL 232089; see page 112.

Railway. Station, 1850; see page 128. Note Victorian posting box on up platform. Nast Hyde Halt (TL 206075), Hertfordshire's smallest station.

Tunnel. Ponsbourne tunnel TL 315076–TL 309053; see page 132.

Bridges. TL 232104, carrying main line out of King's Cross; see page 131.

Aviation. De Havilland Aircraft Co Ltd airfield and factory established 1930; Hawker Siddeley Aviation Ltd, 1963; see page 25.

HEMEL HEMPSTEAD AND BOXMOOR

New Town. Designated a Government-sponsored New Town in 1949; its Development Corporation has now given place to the New Towns Commission.

Mill. Picott's End (TL 050092); see page 51.

Papermaking. (1) Frogmore (TL 059015); present building 1863; see pages 56 and 61; (2) Apsley End (TL 062051); see page 58.

Gas works. Boxmoor Gas Co formed 1866, now Eastern Gas Board. Gas holder 1904, engineer's house about 1880. Two gas standards, one outside Boxmoor Hall, the other in High Street; see page 91.

Bridge. Decorative iron footbridge in Gadebridge Park; see pages 114, 125.

Inns. King's Arms, a late eighteenth-century amalgamation of two seventeenth-century inns, together having in 1756 stabling for 58 horses. Fishery Inn, formerly had stabling for canal horses.

Railway. Two bridges: (1) Queensway; see page 133; (2) Boxmoor, carrying main line over A41, two skew bridges side by side, 1838 and 1875, one brick, one iron girder, each with two tracks. Of the brick bridge John Britton FSA in his Introduction to J. C. Bourne's *Drawings of the London and Birmingham Railway* (1838) says: 'Considered to be the finest specimen of an oblique or skew bridge yet constructed.'

Canal. Wharves (TL 045062 and TL 064051); see page 120.

HERTFORD

Maltings. Nine not operating. (1) north-west corner of bus station, pre-1881; (2) Bull Plain, 1839(?); (3) Old Cross, with sixteenth-century brick at base of one building; (4) Port Vale, pre-1881 (demolished 1969); (5) Priory Street, about 1875 (illustrated on page 38); (6) Railway Place, about 1864; (7) Railway Street, early nineteenth century; (8) St Aldrew Street, about 1838; (9) West Street, 1852.

Mills. (1) Sele Mill, mostly 1891 but part 1822, still working; (2) Brickendon, Horns Mill, contains fulling stocks; see page 76.

Gas works. Hertfordshire's oldest gas works; see page 85.

Water works. Lea Valley Water Co has three installations formerly operated by Hertford Corporation: Port Hill pumping station and reservoir, about 1840; Hartham Lane pumping station, built 1862, rebuilt 1900; Molewood pumping station, a rebuilding in 1880 of a former water mill, has 'J. Bell 1800' on a stone in one of its walls. See page 97.

Brewery. Messrs McMullen; see page 46.

New River. Chadwell Spring (TL 350137), one of the two headsprings, now dry, of the New River, 1608, surrounded by eighteenth-century boundary stones. Broadmead pumping station, 1881. Intake Gauge from river Lea, 1856; see page 99.

Coaching inns. Salisbury Arms (medieval foundations), Dimsdale Arms (probably closed 1770 or 71) and White Hart (both pre-1621), altogether had stabling for 106 horses in 1756. A former inn in Fore

Street, now a chemist's shop, still has what used to be a small coach-ticket office in its side wall.

Brickfield. At Stonyhills (TL 321172). All equipment modern; see page 20.

Bridge. Folly Bridge, at the bottom of Bull Plain (TL 326128), rebuilt 1860. Terminal point of Lea Navigation.

Railway. Cowbridge Station offices, closed 1951; now dwelling houses; East Station, 1888, has fluted iron columns holding electric buffer lights; see page 128. The original Hertford station, 1843, at the bottom of Railway Place, after becoming a goods terminal, was demolished in 1964. Viaduct over Lea, 1920 (TL 320113); see page 132.

HERTINGFORDBURY

Mill. Rebuilt in the late nineteenth century and working until 1933, now a store. Wheel.

Wellheads. Simple wellhead, probably about 1890, on Birch Green (TL 292117), Cole Green (TL 281116), East End Green (TL 297109), Letty Green (TL 284111), and Staines Green (TL 296118).

Railway. Hertingfordbury and Cole Green station offices both converted to dwelling houses.

Woolmers. Built by the Duke of Bridgewater about 1800, when he was contemplating an extensive system embracing the rivers Lea and Stort; architect J. Lewis. Replaces earlier house occupied in the 1760s by John Collins, calico printer. See page 21.

HEXTON

Village pump. Iron, handle-type pump, erected in 1846, reopened for use in 1934 but not now used; surmounted by modern gas lantern; see page 91.

Posting box. Wall posting box; see page 135.

HITCHIN

Malting. Corner of Charlton Road and Wratten Road, mostly

timber with tiled roof but has sixteenth-century brick at its base; a building of the same shape stood there in 1700. Kiln has been demolished; now a builder's yard.

Mills. (1) Charlton Mill (TL 178280), only wheel remains after fire destroyed the mill in 1887; (2) Grove Mill (TL 192205), partly about 1814, partly 1889, milling until about 1908, now factory and offices. For its short use as a silk mill see page 67; (3) Purwell Mill, 1861, now a private house; (4) Station Mills, early twentieth century; (5) West Mill, Oughton Head (TL 171208), burnt down 1961 but race and sluice remain; mill house probably early eighteenth century with early nineteenth-century stabling.

Gas engine. In the workshops of F. Newton, builder and contractor, a Crossley horizontal, single-cylinder engine with twin fly wheels and hot fuel ignition. Not serviced 'for many years' and still in daily use (plate, page 89).

Coaching inn. The Sun, in existence in 1575, much enlarged in the eighteenth century. Extensive stabling. Its yard formerly contained a chalybeate spring.

Railway. Station 1850, slate-roofed, iron canopy over entrance; up platform has 1850 foliated design in canopy spandrels.

Bessemer. Sir Henry Bessemer (1813–98) was born in Charlton House (TL 179281).

HODDESDON

Malting. Formerly attached to Christie's Brewery, most of which was demolished in 1928 and the rest more recently. Late nineteenth century but now very much altered.

New River. Pumping stations: (1) Rye Common (TL 380111), built 1882; (2) Essex Road (TL 378090), built 1865. Bridges: (1) The Lynch (TL 377086), built 1842; (2) Spitalbrook (TL 374080); (3) Spitalbrook (TL 374076); see page 101.

McAdam. In the house in High Street now occupied by Lloyd's Bank, John Loudon McAdam (1756–1836) lived from 1825 until the year of his death. There is a tablet to him in Broxbourne church.

HUNTON BRIDGE

Mill. (TQ 084998); see pages 48 and 95.

ICKLEFORD

Mill. Part 1832, part 1898, part modern. Wheelhouse but no wheel. Still working, now using electric power.

Bridge. (TL 189323). Cadwell Bridge over river Hiz, 1844, when it divided (as stated on plaque in south parapet) Ickleford, Herts, from Holwell, then in Beds.

KIMPTON

Malting. Formerly part of nineteenth-century brewery of Kingsley, later Chalkley; then village hall and now part of laundry. Very much altered.

Mill. (TL 198184). Working until about 1930 and now a private house.

KING'S LANGLEY

Malting. Built for Groome's Brewery (now demolished) in 1826, now church hall. Brick and flint chequered, kiln demolished.

Mill. Probably mostly nineteenth century but very difficult to date. Still working.

Papermaking. (1) Home Park Mills (TL 078021) built by John Dickinson in 1826 but mostly modern. Undershot wheel removed 1960 but used steam power from first building; (2) Nash Mills (TL 069045) taken over by John Dickinson in 1811 but now all modern except Regency millhouse in which Dickinson lived after marriage; see pages 59–60.

Bridge. (TL 071040). Carrying old London and North Western main line over Grand Union Canal; see page 121. J. C. Bourne's *Drawings of the London and Birmingham Railway* (1838) shows it in its original state.

KING'S WALDEN

Windmill. Breachwood Green (TL 146252); see page 52.

KNEBWORTH

Bridge. TL 248208, over main line out of King's Cross; see page 115.

LEMSFORD

Mill. Rebuilt 1863, working until about 1905, now engineering works. Wheel.

Bridge. Carrying pre-1833 line of Great North Road over river Lea; built about 1800; typical of small turnpike trust bridges all over the county.

LETCHWORTH

Garden City. England's first Garden City, founded by Ebenezer (later Sir Ebenezer) Howard in 1903. It was planned and has developed as a self-contained town with separated but closely related areas for industrial and residential purposes, the whole being surrounded by a belt of open country. Much development since the Second World War.

Mill. Norton Mill (TL 236351) rebuilt in the nineteenth century. By 1902 described as a fishery and now a private house.

LITTLE GADDESDEN

Water works. Built 1856; see page 97.

LITTLE HADHAM

Windmill. (TL 438229). Smock mill; see page 52.

LONDON COLNEY

Bridge. (TL 182037). Over river Colne; see page 113.

LONG MARSTON

Railway. Station (SP 885161) on Leighton Buzzard–Aylesbury branch line, opened in 1839, closed in 1952. Brick and timber buildings, track removed, derelict. Victorian posting box close by.

NORTH MYMMS

Milestone. Bell Bar (TL 256051) outside Swan Cottage, stone milestone with inscribed date 1745; see page 110.

NEWNHAM

Village pump. On village green; see page 93.

OFFLEY

Village pump. Near crossroads in middle of village; see page 93.

PARK STREET

Mills. (1) Park Street Mill, about 1846, two wheels, working until First World War, now apparently unoccupied.
Railway. Station wholly of wood with wooden platform on stilts. Line opened 1858.

POTTERS BAR

Coaching inn. Green Man, seventeenth century, demolished 1969.
Horse trough. Alongside A1000 (TL 253993).
Tunnel. On main line out of King's Cross, TL 256004–TL 261994; see page 131.

PRESTON

Village pump. See page 93.

PUCKERIDGE

Coaching inn. Crown and Falcon, an amalgamation of two inns in the eighteenth century. Pepys stayed at the Falcon (the present premises) in 1662. Extensive stabling.
Milestone. In Hamels Park (TL 382243); see page 111.

RADLETT

Bridge. TL 167995; see page 114.
Railway. Station, 1868.

REDBOURN

Mill. Redbournbury Mill (TL 118108); see page 50.
Silk mill. Now Brooke Bond Tea Ltd; see page 67.
Wellhead gears. (1) Dane End Farm (TL 105105); see page 94; (2) Old Jeromes (TL 104098), wood, wheel of 5 ft 6 in diameter, 3½ in wide, wooden spindle directly above well; dating difficult.
Coaching inn. Bull, in existence in 1595, with stabling for 80 horses in 1744 and later a halt for all coaches passing along Watling Street to the north-west. Kept in 1802 by Joseph, and in 1815 by Catherine Stephens, whose son Henry, a doctor, was the inventor of Stephens's blue-black ink.

REED

Windmill. Mile End Farm (TL 359386), tower mill, one storey demolished, new copper cap, no sails, condition indifferent.

RICKMANSWORTH

Papermaking. (1) Croxley Mills (TQ 084954), built by John Dickinson in 1830; original Egyptian style frontage, designed by the wish of Lord Ebury, who owned the land, now embedded in modern building; (2) Scotsbridge Mill (TQ 065952), operating from 1755 to 1885, now almost entirely rebuilt and used as repair and despatch depot by MGM pictures.
Water works. Brick building with stone window heads and pediment (1881 on keystone above principal door) incorporated in the works of the Rickmansworth and Uxbridge Valley Water Co.
Horse trough. TQ 055994.
Railway. Metropolitan station, 1887.
Canal. Stocker's bridge (TQ 052935); see page 121. Gasworks arm and lifting bridge; see page 121.

ROYSTON

Malting. Near station, about 1860, but much altered and now in industrial occupation.

Brewery. Formerly Phillips Ltd, now wholesale confectionery manufacturers; mostly rebuilt but eighteenth-century house at gates separately owned and occupied.

Mill. Large steam mill, 1864, near station. Still working on soya products.

Gas works. See page 88.

Coaching inn. Bull, in existence in 1520 but now with Victorian frontage. Stabling for more than 100 horses in 1772.

ST ALBANS

Maltings. (1) Attached to former Kingsbury Brewery, now Verulam Motors Ltd, Verulam Road; (2) Sopwell Lane, mid or late nineteenth century, now paper store (TL 147069), demolished 1969.

Brewery Kingsbury Brewery, Verulam Road, now Verulam Motors Ltd. Probably rebuilt on change of ownership in 1815, working until end of century.

Mills. (1) Abbey Mills, silk mill from 1804 to 1938; see page 66; (2) Kingsbury Mill, St Michael's; see page 50; (3) New Barnes Mill, rebuilt about 1890, now offices and workshops; (4) Shafford Mill (TL 126093), nineteenth century, no record of working after 1882, now store for stud farm; (5) Sopwell Mill, rebuilt about 1890, paper mill in the seventeenth century, then corn mill working until Second World War, now private house. Contains some gear and an outside wheel of 13 ft diameter, 6 ft 6 in width.

Gas works. Gas holder 1901; see page 87.

Water works. Colne Valley Water Co station on Sandridge Road has a boiler house 1869–74 and foreman's house of same date, now empty. Two iron tanks, both by G. T. Seeley of London (?), one with wrought-iron bands, capacity 82 thousand gallons, 1873, the other wrought-iron, but no steel bands, capacity 170 thousand gallons, 1888.

Donkey wheel. Horizontal donkey wheel at Gorhambury (TL 111078); see page 96.

Coaching inns. Peahen, Red Lion and White Hart are the chief survivors among the many coaching inns of the place. They had stabling for 100 horses in 1756.

Bridge. St Michael's bridge over the river Ver; see page 112.

Railway. Stations: (1) Abbey, canopy over track and platform removed 1967; (2) City, 1868; (3) London Road, offices used as dwelling houses. Bridges: (1) London Road, carrying old Midland main line; (2) close by, also carrying old Midland line over closed Hatfield–St Albans branch. See page 130.

City Museum. Hatfield Road. Contains Salaman collection of tools, blacksmith's, cooper's and wheelwright's shops and tools used in such local crafts as straw-hat making.

ST PAUL'S WALDEN

Mill. Whitwell Mill, nineteenth-century timber on brick base, house modern. Wheel but mill race silted up.

SARRATT

Papermaking. Sarratt Mill (TQ 036980) was making paper between 1744 and about 1781 but, apart from the millhouse, only a small empty building alongside the river Chess remains; see page 55.

Village pump. See page 93.

SAWBRIDGEWORTH

Malting. H. A. & D. Taylor Ltd; see page 34.

Mill. Rebuilt about 1880 when it was converted to steam. It also has a malting. Millhouse eighteenth century. Still operating.

SHENLEY

Aviation. In 1939 the Mosquito aircraft was designed and the prototype built at Salisbury Hall; see page 26.

Silk. Silkworm farm at Salisbury Hall (TL 197028). Sir Nigel Gresley lived at the Hall with his brother in the early 1930s.

STANDON

Mill. Small portions of Old Mill on east bank of river Rib, burnt down in 1961, now factory. New Mill on west bank 1901, still working on soya products.

Papermaking. Standon Mill (TL 392221), after 1855 a sawmill, then engineer's workshop. Fragments of undershot wheel and other gear. Adjoining millhouse seventeenth century. See page 55.

Explosive works. Barwick Ford (TL 384195); see page 81.

STANSTEAD ABBOTS

Maltings. (1) Roydon Road, one possibly about 1840, the other modern, still working; (2) on east bank of river Lea, about 1840, now closed (illustrated on page 17); (3) on west bank of river Lea, 1898, now closed.

Mill. Roydon Road, rebuilt 1861, steam about 1890, ceased milling 1926, now offices and workshops.

STANSTEAD ST MARGARET'S

Malting. Three maltings (TL 380121), each with two kilns, also brick tower and dwelling house. Built about 1866. Now animal food store.

New River. Bridge (TL 379118); see page 101.

Railway. Station; see page 128.

STEVENAGE

New Town. The first Government-sponsored New Town after the passing of the Act of 1946. Now under New Towns Commission.

Gas works. Sish Lane, 1855–1933; see page 88.

Coaching inn. White Lion, rebuilt 1962; had stabling for 30 horses in 1772.

Bridges. Five bridges, all 1850, carrying side roads over the old Great Northern main line in rather less than a mile. Of that at Six Hills (TL 237237) the approaches were demolished in 1907.

Railway. Station, two island platforms joined by footbridge, wooden platform buildings, brick booking hall at road level. Attractively unsophisticated *vis-à-vis* the modern New Town, but likely to be rebuilt.

TEWIN

Mill. Only the race and millhouse, now a private house, remain. Optical glass grinding factory for half the eighteenth century; see page 21.

Bridge. Poplars Green (TL 282133), brick, 1801, part of road diversion by Earl Cowper when building mansion of Panshanger (demolished 1956).

THORLEY

Mill. Twyford Mill (TL 493193), working until Second World War and converted into flats in 1954.

TONWELL

Mill. (TL 338163). Part of wooden wheel has been preserved in its original position; see page 48.

Bridge. Over river Rib (TL 338164), dated 1792; see page 112.

TRING

Maltings. Both in Akeman Street: (1) part of former Rodwell Brewery, 1876; (2) in premises of F. & R. G. Grace, eighteenth and nineteenth centuries but site possibly medieval in origin; see page 37.

Brewery. Brown's Brewery, High Street, 1830, now slaughterhouse; eighteenth-century brewer's house now a butcher's shop. Arched doorway to yard.

Mill. New Mills, rebuilt 1875 for steam, still working. A windmill adjacent to the site—Gamnel Mill—was taken down in 1911.

Windmill. Goldfield Mill (SP 915118), tower mill built about 1852, operating until about 1908; cap but no sails.

Silk mill. Brook Street; see page 67. Note waterwheel, 22 ft diameter, 6 ft width.

L

Coaching inn. Rose and Crown, in existence 1620; in 1852 the booking office of the London and North Western Railway. Rebuilt by Lord Rothschild, 1906.

Milestones. See page 110.

Turnpike post. (SP 919112); see also Berkhamsted and Watford.

Canal. A cutting 382 ft above sea level and 1¼ miles long carries the Grand Union Canal through the Chiltern escarpment. Constructed 1800; see page 119. Wharf at Dudswell (SP 966097); see page 120. Bridges on Aylesbury arm at Dixon's Gap (SP 909145) and Wilstone (SP 905144); see page 112.

Railway. Station: 1838 ticket office at ground level demolished in 1966, see page 127; wooden platform buildings. Tring cutting; see page 130.

WADESMILL

Bridge. Carries A10 over the river Rib; see page 113.

Coaching inn. The Feathers, in existence in 1617, said to have had stabling for 100 horses in the early nineteenth century.

WALKERN

Malting and brewery. See page 43.

Mill. TL 286254; rebuilt in 1828, ceased working in 1933 and now derelict. Note initials and dates on south wall.

WARE

Maltings. One operating: Victoria Maltings, Amwell End, built 1907, enlarged and modernised 1936 and 1948, large new building 1966.

Eleven not operating: (1) Amwell End, Hoo Lane, about 1824, kiln with wire mesh flooring, now a factory; (2) Amwell End, London Road, possibly about 1839, derelict; (3) Church Street, Alma Maltings, 1855; (4) Church Street, south side, with kiln, about 1845; (5) Coronation Street, largely rebuilt on conversion into industrial premises; (6) no 16 Crib Street, with kiln, standing in 1845; (7) High Street, Priory Maltings, partly demolished but kiln remains, standing in 1845; (8) behind no 63 High Street, probably about 1870; (9) near Kybes Lane, with kilns and windbreaker cowls, standing in 1845; (10) Star Street, south side, part standing in 1845, part rebuilt about 1900; (11) Watton Road, Crooks Yard, south end, with kiln, standing in 1845.

Brewery. Star Brewery, Watton Road, built 1862, now a store.

Mills. (1) Station Mills, built 1896, still working; (2) Ware Mills, probably mostly early nineteenth century, ceased milling 1899, now Allen & Hanbury Ltd.

Gasworks. See page 88.

New River. Pumping stations, Amwell Hill, 1847; Amwell End, 1867; Amwell Marsh, 1883; see page 100.

Railway. (1) Station, 1843, portico'd entrance, single platform, goods shed with fanlighted window heads; (2) Mardock station (Wareside) (TL 392148), with single platform and wooden station building on closed St Margaret's–Buntingford line, now derelict; see page 129.

WATERFORD

Bridges. Carrying side road over river Beane (TL 315157), 1870; three bridges on A602 near Goldings at TL 314141, TL 314137 and TL 314135, all 1869; see page 113.

WATFORD

The industrial expansion of Watford from 1800 onwards is outlined in Chapter Six.

Malting. No 239 High Street, standing in 1872 but nothing known of it; now a garage.

Brewery. Benskin's Watford Brewery, High Street; see page 152.

Mill. Grove Mill (TQ 088986), rebuilt about 1875, working until 1922, now a store.

Papermaking. Hamper Mill (TQ 097940), operating 1776–1908.

Several times partially rebuilt and now a private house but with eighteenth-century millhouse.

Silk mill. Rookery Mill (TQ 107951); see pages 66, 140, 145.

Gas works. See pages 86, 87, 141.

Water Works. See pages 92, 94, 97.

Turnpike post. (TQ 118955). See also Berkhamsted and Tring.

Canal. Bridge: approach road to the Grove at TQ 087988; see page 121.

Railway. Stations: (1) Junction, 1858; (2) High Street, 1868. Both have iron canopies over entrances. Tunnel: TL 087003–TQ 107977 duplicated 1874, 3 airshafts each tunnel; see page 130.

Bridges. (1) Viaduct over river Colne (TL 116966); see page 129; (2) bridge over Water Lane, single-line traffic, headroom 10 ft, high earthen embankment above; (3) also at TQ 089961 and TQ 091962; see page 133.

WATTON-AT-STONE

Mill. Built 1830, ceased milling 1930, then various uses, almost completely demolished 1968.

Village pump. Erected 1895; see page 94.

Milestone. On B1001 at TL 329181; see page 110.

WELWYN

Tollgate cottage. Opposite Ayot Green (TL 223130); see page 109.

Gasworks. Base of small gasholder in present Herts County Council road yard; see page 86.

Coaching inns. Wellington, in existence in 1352, and White Hart, 1675.

Bridge. Lockleys old bridge (TL 236157), carrying now abandoned line of road to Hertford, built about 1834.

Railway. (1) Welwyn or Digswell Viaduct (TL 245148) over Mimram valley; see page 131; (2) Robbery Bottom Viaduct (TL 253183); see page 132; (3) Woolmer Green (TL 251188).

Tunnels. South tunnel, 429 yd; north tunnel, 1047 yd; one air shaft to short tunnel, two to longer; see page 132.

WELWYN GARDEN CITY

England's second Garden City (Hampstead Garden Suburb, London, 1906, does not strictly speaking fall into Garden City category), founded by Ebenezer (later Sir Ebenezer) Howard in 1920 and planned to benefit from the pioneering mistakes made at Letchworth. In 1948 designated a Government-sponsored New Town; its Development Corporation (jointly with Hatfield) has since given place to the New Towns Commission.

WESTMILL

Village pump. Erected about 1900; see page 93.

WESTON

Windmill. Lannock Mill (TL 252305), tower mill built about 1860, working until about 1922, no cap or sails; see page 52.

WHEATHAMPSTEAD

Maltings. (1) Behind High Street, standing in 1840, now private house and much altered; (2) Brewhouse Hill, probably about 1870, still has kiln, now a factory.

Mills. (1) Batford Mill (TL 148150), probably about 1860 but partly rebuilt, millhouse possibly eighteenth century, now a factory; (2) Bridge Mill, partly eighteenth century or possibly rather earlier but many alterations and additions, still working; (3) East Hyde Mill (TL 132170), built 1835, one wheel still occasionally working, some nineteenth-century equipment; see page 50.

Papermaking. Pickford Mill (TL 143155), now entirely rebuilt as a factory, only the name remaining.

Railway. Station, ground-level booking office, platform and line on embankment; nineteenth-century goods shed adjoining. Line closed 1965.

Wellhead gear. The Laurels, Wheathampstead Hill; plunger-type under canopy by Hayward Taylor; see page 94.

WIGGINTON

Canal. Cow Roast Lock (SP 959103), 328 ft above sea level; see page 119.

WORMLEY

New River. Bridge (TL 364037), built 1841.

London Coal Duty Boundary Markers

Alongside railways: stone obelisk

TL 368052   Wormley. Broken
TL 243028   North Mymms, Hawkshead. In position
TQ 117967   Watford, below viaduct over Colne. Broken

Alongside railways: iron obelisk

TL 159008   Radlett, N end of the Avenue
TQ 114919   Oxhey, Little Oxhey Lane. Not near railway
TQ 091921   Northwood (Middlesex). On embankment

Alongside waterways

TL 372050   Wormley. Lea Navigation
TQ 046932   Rickmansworth. Grand Union Canal

Alongside roads

TL 364056   Wormley. On A10
TL 343058   Wormley–Cheshunt boundary, ½ m N of Paradise Hill
TL 304042   Hatfield, ½ m SE of Newgate Street
TL 300042   Hatfield, ½ m S of Newgate Street and N of Carbone Hill
TL 272035   Northaw, W end of Ridgeway
TL 270032   Northaw, entrance to Queenswood drive
TL 260021   Potters Bar. On A1000
TL 260021   Potters Bar, Church Road. These two markers are within a hundred yards of each other
TL 257025   Potters Bar, Hawkshead road
TL 250031   North Mymms, S end of Water Lane

TL 205058	Colney Heath, road crossing
TL 205959	Colney Heath, opposite Cock public house
TL 205050	Colney Heath, near Coursers Farm
TL 199059	Colney Heath, near gravel pits
TL 182037	London Colney, alongside bridge carrying A6
TL 176032	London Colney, Broad Colney bridge
TL 172023	Shenley, near Colneyhouse Farm
TL 171020	Shenley, near Harperbury Hospital
TL 170511	Shenley, in hedge on Wild Farm
TQ 165995	Radlett, High Street
TQ 161005	Radlett, on A5 $\frac{1}{2}$ m N of station
TQ 151939	Watford, Bushey Heath, on A4140
TQ 131926	Oxhey, on A4008 at Burntwood Farm
TQ 120925	Bushey, Capell Road near station
TQ 118955	Bushey, NE corner of Bushey Arches
TQ 116963	Watford, Water Lane. Re-erected 1966 at College of Further Education
TQ 106916	Oxhey, on B468 at Potterstreet Hill–Oxhey Drive Junction
TQ 087923	Rickmansworth, in playing fields of school S of Batchworth Lane
TQ 078924	Rickmansworth, Batchworth Heath near Prince of Wales public house
TQ 070915	Rickmansworth, junction of White Hill and Jackets Lane
TQ 069915	Rickmansworth, Battlewells Farm
TQ 065917	Rickmansworth, Battlewells Farm N of old reservoir
TQ 059922	Rickmansworth, Woodcock Hill–Harefield road
TQ 041935	Rickmansworth, bridge over Colne near Drayton Ford
TQ 044935	Rickmansworth, junction of Shire Ditch and Colne S of Stockers Lake
Note	
TQ 052934	Rickmansworth. Originally at Stockers Farm (this Nat Grid ref), re-erected at Shepherds School, 1964

Milestones

THE present position of milestones is listed here. Some, however, were moved from an earlier site on a past re-routing of their section of road—St Albans, Batchwood cross is an example. Others (eg St Albans, Barnards Heath) were left on the abandoned route. At Welwyn there are three 25th milestones—one (cast iron) in Church Street, two (one stone, one cast iron) on the Codicote road, A600. The stone one was slightly changed in position in 1956.

The historical interest of milestones will be increased, and the recording of their sites more important still, when road distances come to be measured in kilometres.

Cheshunt Trust (A 10)

TL 356147   Ware, Baldock Road
TL 352138   Hertford, on A119, trust spur road

Dunstable–St Albans Trust (A5)

TL 055173   Markyate Cell
TL 103132   Redbourn, N of village
TL 111117   Redbourn, opposite Chequers public house
TL 118102   Redbourn, near Punch Bowl public house
TL 127008   St Albans, Bow Bridge
TL 137078   St Albans, Batchwood crossroads

Galley Corner Trust (A1000)

TL 232087   Hatfield station yard
TL 228075   Hatfield, Oxlease turn
TL 237060   Hatfield, S end of Milwards Park

TL 252054   North Mymms, Bell Bar. Two stones (see page 110)
TL 239041   Brookmans Park, S of Kentish Lane
TL 262026   Little Heath, N end of village

Hatfield–Reading Trust (A414, A405, A412, A404)
TL 212084   Hatfield, Ellenbrook
TL 198078   Smallford, near Four Horseshoes public house
TL 183073   St Albans, near Oaklands
TL 165073   St Albans, Fleetville, cemetery
TL 157077   St Albans, opposite Marlborough Almshouses
TL 142062   St Albans, St Stephen's Hill
TQ 995055   Rickmansworth, near entrance to Masonic Schools

Pinner Trust (A404)
TQ 069929   Rickmansworth, road to Batchworth Heath

St Albans–South Mimms Trust (A6)
TL 203026   Ridge Hill. Two stones
TL 168055   St Albans, S of Old Milehouse public house

Luton–St Albans Trust (A6)
TL 151091   St Albans, Barnards Heath, Old Harpenden Road
TL 148100   St Albans, opposite Childwickbury Park
TL 138120   Harpenden, Beeson End turn
TL 136135   Harpenden, near Rothamsted new building

Sparrows Herne Trust (A414, A41)
SP 928115   Tring, near Upper Dunsley
SP 914113   Tring, outside Pendley Park

Stevenage–Bigglesware Trust (B197)
TL 245323   Baldock, near George IV public house
TL 240307   Letchworth, near Letchworth Gate

TL 234293	Letchworth, S of Jack's Hill
TL 231227	Graveley, S end of village
TL 232261	Stevenage, near Rectory Lane

Wadesmill Trust (A10, B1368)

On A10:

TL 359117	Wadesmill, N of village
TL 366192	High Cross, N of village
TL 377222	Standon, opposite St Edmund's College grounds
TL 385234	Puckeridge, High Street
TL 377278	Puckeridge, Hamels Park. See page 111
TL 371278	Puckeridge, N of Hamels Park
TL 364292	Buntingford, S end of town
TL 363293	Buntingford, outside St Peter's Church
TL 356308	Buntingford, opposite Corneybury
TL 355324	Chipping, N of village
TL 356356	Reed, N of Reed turn
TL 358372	Reed
TL 358388	Reed, N of windmill
TL 357404	Royston, S end

On B1368:

TL 382248	Braughing, near bridge over stream
TL 392265	Hay Street
TL 393280	Dassells Hill
TL 390296	Hare Street
TL 392311	
TL 389327	Anstey, Cave Gate
TL 386341	
TL 385356	Barkway, High Street; see page 110
TL 393339	Barkway, Newsells Park
TL 397382	Barley, opposite the shop at the corner
TL 402398	Barley, county boundary

Watton Trust (A602, B1001)

On A602:

TL 305142   Waterford, opposite Goldings
TL 311158   Waterford, near Bullsmill turn
TL 304191   Watton, S end
TL 227208   Watton, N of Horseshoes public house

On B1001:

TL 329181   Sacombe, opposite Burrs Green turn. See page 110

Welwyn Trust (A1, B197, A600)

On A1 and B 197:

TL 222135   Welwyn Garden City, opposite Brockswood Lane
TL 222149   Welwyn, Digswell Hill
TL 232162   Welwyn, Church Street
TL 245175   Welwyn, Oaklands
TL 253186   Woolmer Green
TL 250202   Knebworth cross roads
TL 247219   Knebworth, S of Broadwater

On A600:

TL 231163   Welwyn, outside Guessens
TL 231164   Welwyn, just N of above
TL 221178   Codicote, S end
TL 214181   Codicote, opposite Mansells Lane

Non-turnpike

TL 011009   Near Little Gaddesden
TL 002119   Near Little Gaddesden
             See page 111 for both these milestones

Victorian Posting Boxes

Pillar Boxes

1879–83	TL 055078	Hemel Hempstead Town Hall
1883–7	TL 137143	Harpenden, Station Road
1887–1901	TL 003055	Bovingdon RAF Station
	TL 142147	Harpenden, Browning Road
	TL 219338	Letchworth, Southfields
	TL 162074	St Albans, Glenferrie Road
	TL 178072	St Albans, Oaklands PO
	TL 175034	St Albans, Napsbury Sub-PO
	TL 305251	Walkern, Clay End

Wall Boxes

1859–61	TL 028114	Great Gaddesden, brick pillar
	TL 106104	Hexton, wall of Sub-PO
1861–71	TL 146985	Aldenham, Round Bush, house wall
	TL 325254	Ardeley, Wood End, brick pillar
	SP 980072	Berkhamsted, Shooters Way–Cross Oak crossing, brick pillar in wall
	TL 006032	Bovingdon, Halfway, brick pillar near Halfway public house
	TL 397382	Barley, The Mount, brick pillar near Chequers public house
	TL 368108	Great Amwell, Lower Hailey Lane, house wall
	TL 042068	Hemel Hempstead, Green End Lane, brick pillar
	TL 055078	Hemel Hempstead, High Street, shop wall

	TL 054155	Markyate, Cheverells Park, near gateway
	SP 012062	Northchurch, Bourne End, roadside wall
	TL 360414	Royston, Melbourne Road, house wall
	TQ 031991	Sarratt Bottom, brick pillar
	TQ 067001	Sarratt, Little Westwood, cottage wall
	TQ 039984	Sarratt, Church End, cottage wall
	TL 213226	Stevenage, Titmore Green, brick pillar
	TL 176139	Wheathampstead, Brewhouse Hill, brick pillar
	TL 192202	Whitwell Hoo Farm, farmhouse wall
1871–81	TL 293383	Ashwell, Odsey, brick pillar
	TL 045099	Great Gaddesden, Grist House Farm, wall
	TL 242067	Hatfield Woodside, wall of lodge
	TL 267059	Hatfield Woodfield, churchyard wall
	SP 996096	Northchurch, Dudswell, wall of Bastwick House
	SP 894150	Puttenham, Astrope, brick pillar
	TL 236360	Radwell, garden wall
	TL 100118	Redbourn, Church End, shop wall
	TQ 071962	Rickmansworth, Croxley Green, brick pillar
	TL 178144	Wheathampstead station
	TL 177157	Wheathampstead, Gustard Wood, house wall
	TL 168146	Wheathampstead, The Folly, shop wall
	SP 924111	Tring, no 42 Akeman Street, house wall
1881–	TL 090021	Abbots Langley, Abbots Road, brick pillar
	TL 222144	Ayot St Peter, old station approach, brick pillar
	TL 408240	Braughing, Upp Hall, brick pillar
	TL 192953	Boreham Wood, Deacons Hill, garden wall
	TQ 138945	Bushey, Merry Hill Mount, shop wall
	TL 365045	Cheshunt, Turnford High Road, shop wall
	TL 366024	Cheshunt, Windmill Lane, railway station

TL 334024	Cheshunt, Goffs Oak, Halstead Lane, brick pillar
TL 035025	Chipperfield, Tower Hill, brick pillar.
TL 214064	Colney Heath, Roestock Green, brick pillar
TL 262084	Essendon, West End, brick pillar in wall
TL 076140	Flamstead, Trowley Bottom, brick pillar
TL 445279	Furneux Pelham, wall of Bonhams
TL 064118	Great Gaddesden, Stagsden, wall of Hawbush Farm
TL 358223	Great Munden, Levens Green, brick pillar
TL 136138	Harpenden, Coach Lane, West Common, house wall
TL 232087	Hatfield station, up platform
TL 276099	Hatfield, Holwell Manor, garden wall
TL 255110	Hatfield, Stanborough Green, wall of Stanborough Lodge
TL 035064	Hemel Hempstead, Chaulden Lane, brick pillar
TL 063050	Hemel Hempstead, wall of Apsley Mills
TL 292117	Hertingfordbury, Birch Green, school wall
TL 181294	Hitchin, Bedford Road, shop wall
TL 068028	King's Langley, Vicarage Lane, garden wall
TL 240202	Knebworth old village, brick pillar
TL 231344	Letchworth, Norton, brick pillar in churchyard wall
TL 295085	Little Berkhampstead, Robins Nest Hill, brick pillar
SP 885167	Long Marston, Marston Gate station, brick pillar
TQ 120951	Oxhey, Pinner Road, house wall
TL 144323	Pirton, Burge End, brick pillar
TL 204024	Potters Bar, Osborne Road, Little Heath, brick pillar in garden wall

	TL 162993	Radlett, Scrubbits Square, house wall
	TQ 034911	Rickmansworth, West Hyde, brick pillar by Sub-PO
	TL 203070	St Albans, Sleapshyde, brick pillar opposite Plough public house
	TL 220270	St Ippollitts, brick pillar opposite church
	TL 193223	St Paul's Walden, brick pillar in churchyard wall
	TL 490150	Sawbridgeworth, opposite station
	TL 237256	Stevenage, Walkern Road, brick pillar
	TL 268241	Stevenage, Aston End, brick pillar
	SP 927121	Tring, Brook Street, brick pillar
	TL 105984	Watford, Leavesden Road, wall of school playground
	TL 177135	Wheathampstead, The Hill, garden wall
	TL 176127	Wheathampstead, Nomansland, brick pillar outside Wicked Lady Hotel
Adapted	TL 332054	Cheshunt, Beaumonts Manor, brick pillar
c 1960	TL 045112	Great Gaddesden, Bridens Camp, brick pillar
	TL 041049	Hemel Hempstead, Bulstrode Lane, Felden, wall of outbuilding
	TL 057079	Hemel Hempstead, Midland Road, garden wall
	TL 057078	Hemel Hempstead, Herbert Street, brick pillar in house wall
	SP 993138	Tring, Bulbourne, wall of Grand Junction Arms public house

Lamp Boxes

1896–	TL 036016	Chipperfield, Dunny Lane, wooden post
	TQ 035960	Chorley Wood, Black Horse public house, wooden post

TL 184262	Hitchin, Gosmore, Tatmore Place, wooden post
TL 169234	King's Walden, Whitehall Farm, wooden post
TL 020105	Nettleden, wooden post
TL 134268	Offley, The Flints, telegraph pole
TL 126089	Redbourn, Bow Bridge, telegraph pole
TL 344060	Wormley West End, telegraph pole

Note

Pillar boxes with Edward VIII cipher:

TQ 025961	Chorley Wood, Haddon Road
TL 302031	Cuffley, junction of Tolmers Road and Oak Lane
TL 316125	Hertford, near Hertford North station, A602.
TL 175071	St Albans, Cambridge Road, Hill End

M

Bibliography

PARTLY, no doubt, because of its age-long agricultural tradition but also for the reasons suggested in my Acknowledgments, very little appears to have been written on the industrial archaeology of Hertfordshire and this bibliography of the publications I have most frequently consulted is distressingly thin. Some incidental references to others do, however, appear in the text. Other sources outside my knowledge there may well be; frankly, my chief source has been my own survey of the county's industrial monuments and the report that accompanied it. I must admit to not having used magazines and county newspapers to the extent that they deserve but would stress the value to all subsequent workers of much rather scattered material in the Hertfordshire County Record Office, County Hall, Hertford.

GENERAL

Cooke, G. A. *Topographical and Statistical Description of the County of Hertford* (1825)
Cussans, J. E. *History of Hertfordshire* (1870–81)
Freeling, A. *Railway Companion London to Birmingham* (1841)
Gardner, H. W. *Survey of the Agriculture of Hertfordshire*, Royal Agricultural Society of England (1967)
Hassall, John. *Picturesque Rides 30 Miles round the British Metropolis* (1817–18); *Tour of the Grand Junction Canal* (1819)
Lewis, G. *Topographical Dictionary* (2nd edn, 1849)
Osborne, E. C. *London and Birmingham Railway Guide* (1840)
Victoria County History of Hertfordshire (1902–14)
Young, Arthur. *General View of the Agriculture of Hertfordshire* (1804)

Periodicals:
Journal of Industrial Archaeology and *Industrial Archaeology*, ed by
   Kenneth Hudson
The Amateur Historian (now *The Local Historian*), ed by Lionel M.
   Munby

Directories:
Universal British Directory, 1792; Pigot, 1826–30; Robson, 1838;
   Cassey, 1864; Kelly's Post Office Directory from 1855

MALTING AND BREWING

Barnard, A. *Noted Breweries of the United Kingdom* (1889–91)
Connell, E. J. 'Hertford Breweries', *Industrial Archaeology*, vol 4,
   no 1 (1967)
Hunt, E. M. *History of Ware* (1946)
Mathias, P. *The Brewing Industry of England 1700–1830* (1959)
Taylor, H.A. and D. *Two Hundred Years of Malting* (nd)

MILLS

Wailes, Rex. *The English Windmill* (1954)
Carus Wilson, E. M. 'The development of fulling mills', *Economic
   History Review*, vol XI (1941)
Connell, E. J. 'Early fulling stocks at Hertford', *Hertfordshire Past
   and Present*, No 6 (Hertfordshire Local History Council, 1966)

PAPERMAKING AND PRINTING

Evans, Joan. *The Endless Web* (1955)
Finerty, E. T. 'The history of paper mills in Hertfordshire', *Paper
   Maker* (April, May, June 1957)
Moran, James. *Stephen Austin of Hertford* (1968)
Thwaite, M. F. *Hertfordshire Newspapers* (Hertfordshire Local His-
   tory Council, 1956)

SILK INDUSTRY

Warner, Sir Frank. *The Silk Industry in the United Kingdom* (1921)

STRAW PLAITING

Dony, J. S. *The History of the Straw Hat Industry of Luton* (1942)
Gray, Edwin. *Cottage Life in a Hertfordshire Village* (?1935)
Kalm, P. *An Account of a Visit to England in 1748* (1892)

HERB DISTILLERY

Hine, R. L. *Hitchin Worthies* (1932)

TERRA COTTA WORKS AND BRICKMAKING

Hayllar, H. F. *Chronicles of Hoddesdon* (1948)
Storey, R. 'Hitch's Patent Bricks', *Journal of Industrial Archaeology*,
vol 1, no 4 (1965)

COAL DUTY BOUNDARY MARKERS

Bawtree, M. 'London Coal Duties and their Boundary Markers',
Rickmansworth Historian (Rickmansworth Local History Society,
Autumn 1964)

GAS INDUSTRY

Moore, Cyril. 'The gas industry in North Hertfordshire', in *Hertfordshire Past and Present*, No 5 (Hertfordshire Local History
Council, 1965)

NEW RIVER

Berry, G. C. and Flowerdew, C. J. *London's Water Supply* (1953)
Gough, J. W. *Sir Hugh Myddleton* (1964)
Richardson, A. E. *Robert Mylne* (1955).

WATERWAYS

Hadfield, Charles. *Canals of South and South East England* (1969); *British Canals* (1966)
Hobday, S. and Thacker, F.S. *History of the River Lea* (MS in Hertfordshire County Record Office, nd)
Rolt, L. T. C. *The Inland Waterways of England* (1950)
British Waterways Board Cruising Booklets: no 3, Lea and Stort; no 8, Grand Union Canal, Southern Section

RAILWAYS

Allen, Cecil J. *The Great Eastern Railway* (1955, 4th edn 1967)
Grindling, Charles. *The Great Northern Railway* (1898, new edn 1967)
Simmons, J. *The Railways of England* (1967)
Stratton, C. E. *The London and Birmingham Railway* (2nd edn 1901)

POSTING BOXES

Farrugia, J. Y. *The Letter Box* (1969)

WATFORD

Leach, Marion. *David Greenhill, Master Printer* (1950)
Saunders, W. R. *History of Watford* (1931)
Watford Observer Centenary Supplement, 1963

Acknowledgments

HERTFORDSHIRE is in the unfortunate position of having no university to initiate or encourage the pursuit of industrial archaeology, a *Victoria County History* that is more than half a century old and few archaeological or historical societies to whom the subject appears to have made much appeal. An initial flicker of awareness that it existed as a possible study came in 1963 from the Hertfordshire Local History Council; the first firm step was taken only in 1964, when I was appointed consultant to the Hertfordshire County Council in making a survey of pre-1900 industrial monuments on the lines of the national survey sponsored by the Council for British Archaeology and, at that time, the Ministry of Public Building and Works. Even so, I, an historian and in no sense a technologist, was allowed only two years to complete a pioneer task of unknown magnitude. In spite of the rather despondent tone of the first sentence above, I did, however, find both Mr D. J. Capper, who rapidly became my indispensable right hand, and also a small band of enthusiastic helpers (including the Rickmansworth Historical Society) intimate with their own localities; and in my final Report to the County Council[1] I was glad to acknowledge too the interest shown by the officers of many public bodies and the executives and employees of many industrial concerns. Still, the responsibility for the work of discovery, inspection and research remained mine alone to tackle; and to me personally one great value of this book is that, while enabling me to correct some errors in the survey, it gives me an opportunity of reiterating my thanks to all former helpers as well as offering thanks to new ones, and also of enlarging (I think usefully) upon several topics for which the survey itself gave neither time nor scope.

[1] *Industrial Monuments in Hertfordshire* (Hertfordshire County Record Office, County Hall, Hertford, 1967).

The chapter which breaks rather new ground is that outlining the industrial expansion of Watford since 1800; for material and guidance in its preparation I am grateful to Mr R. C. Sayell, FLA, until recently Watford Borough Librarian, and Miss M. Marshall, in charge of the Reference Room there. For help and advice on canals and waterways I am indebted to Mr C. N. Hadlow, Curator of the British Waterways Museum, Stoke Bruerne, and Mr A. H. Faulkner; on railways to Mr G. N. Webb; on the Hunton Bridge wooden waterwheel to Mr H. W. Hockin; and for identification of one or two leading Hertfordshire silk throwsters to the County Archivist of Cumberland and the Huguenot Society of London.

My thanks are also due to Miss Vivienne C. Jenkins, BSc, who is responsible for the maps and diagrams; but most cordially of all to Mr Rex Wailes, FSA, MIMechE, who has been an invaluable source of technical reference and a most kindly encourager throughout the rather anxious months during which the book has been on my desk.

Index

This index is confined to subjects, individuals and industrial firms. Places having existing sites of industrial archaeological interest are listed in the Gazetteer (pp 157–82); places whose interest is chiefly in the past can be traced by consulting the pages shown in **bold type** in the index. References to plates are printed in *italic*.